D1094737

# ROBOTS, MEN AND MINDS

*Psychology in the Modern World*

*BY THE SAME AUTHOR:*

MODERN THEORIES OF DEVELOPMENT (in German, English, Spanish)

NIKOLAUS VON KUES

LEBENSWISSENSCHAFT UND BILDUNG

THEORETISCHE BIOLOGIE

DAS GEFÜGE DES LEBENS

VOM MOLEKÜL ZUR ORGANISMENWELT

PROBLEMS OF LIFE (in German, English, French, Spanish, Dutch, Japanese)

AUF DEN PFADEN DES LEBENS

BIOPHYSIK DES FLIESSGLEICHGEWICHTS

# ROBOTS, MEN AND MINDS

*Psychology in the Modern World*

**Ludwig von Bertalanffy**
*Professor of Theoretical Biology*
*University of Alberta*
*Edmonton, Canada*

**George Braziller**
*New York*

*Robots, Men and Minds* is based upon The Heinz Werner Inaugural Lectures, presented by the author at Clark University, January 13 and 14, 1966. The original lectures, as delivered, are published by Clark University Press.



For information address the publisher,

*George Braziller, Inc.*
*One Park Avenue*
*New York, N.Y. 10016*

FIRST PRINTING

Library of Congress Catalog Card Number: 67–27524

Printed in the United States of America

# Preface

The present book, as expressed in its title, is concerned with "Psychology in the Modern World." This, perhaps, deserves a word of explanation.

The present Age of Science is marked by the triumphs of physical technology which have earned it the title of a Second Industrial Revolution. Computers, automation, space vehicles, atomic energy and bombs have profoundly changed the world in the past decades. It is less known that innovation in physical technology was paralleled by a phenomenon which is essentially new and unprecedented: the development of a psychological technology which, in the mass society of our days, has consequences no less far-reaching than those following the invention of ever more sophisticated technological "hardware." Physical technology, the control of nature, was supplemented by psychological technology, the control of man himself.

At the same time, the ambivalence of science and technology has become apparent. The menace of thermonuclear war, the population explosion, the social problems in a cybernetic society are commonplace. The historian will note that similar anxieties, though in a minor key, accompanied previous crises such as the invention of airplanes and air raids, the birth pangs of industrialization in the Victorian age, the introduction of firearms in the late Middle Ages, and presumably the appearance of war chariots when peoples from the Asiatic steppes overran the agricultural communities in the Near East at the dawn of history. Doomsday has often been prophesied in the course of history. What appears to be new, however, is that an old intellectual attitude has broken down. Since Bacon of Verulam, the perfectionist philosophers of the eighteenth century, and the belief in progress of the nineteenth, advance of mankind by science and technology was taken for granted. Even earlier, Plato believed that the human predicament was amenable to solution if only philosophers became kings or kings turned into philosophers. That Reason does not automatically lead to a solution of the human problem and, by and large, has little influence in the sanguinary course of human history, was the disappointing discovery of our time. Knowledge is Power, according to Bacon; but has technological power increased human happiness? Is a scientifically controlled society desirable?

Questions of this kind have put the human predicament—in itself as old as man himself—into a new perspective. The present book deals with some aspects of this multifaceted problem: the impact of psychological technology, the underlying problems of human nature and values; and with modern developments which may change our world picture and image of man.

The author, a biologist, is concerned with basic viewpoints, not with specialist critique of particular theories in contemporary psychology (or, for that matter, in his own field of biology). If a fashionable expression is to be used, this essay belongs to "sociology of knowledge," that is, the study of interconnections and interactions between sociocultural situation, science, and world outlook, in a certain period.

The present book is an overview of some main lines of the author's work and thought, as they have developed over some forty-five years; presenting them, without much detail and in non-technical language, within a small compass. It can therefore serve as an introduction to his work which, as he knows well, is dispersed in many places and therefore not easy to see as an organized "system," to borrow a key term of the presentation to follow.

The book is based on lectures delivered as The Inaugural Lectures in The Heinz Werner Lecture Series at Clark University (Worcester, Mass.), in January, 1966. The author wishes to extend his thanks to Clark University, The Heinz Werner Institute of Developmental Psychology and his friend, Dr. Seymour Wapner, Chairman of the Institute, for having given him this opportunity.

Although largely expanding the original presentation in order to convey ideas which could only be intimated or sketched in an oral presentation, the writer tried to preserve the spoken word and its flavor because, hopefully, this permits for freer and more lively expression than the usual style of scientific writing.

Edmonton, May 1967

LUDWIG VON BERTALANFFY

# Contents

# PART ONE

# Toward a New Image of Man

## The Organismic Concept in Psychology and Biology

In a time wavering between contradictory expectations and utopias—mostly of marvels in technology, medicine and society waiting just around the corner, but equally of an atomic Day of Judgment, an earth providing standing room only for teeming humanity, and a cybernetic leisure society which doesn't know exactly what to do with itself—sometimes a look backward is reassuring to establish continuity and to evaluate intellectual trends. Our topic is contemporary psychology contemplated from a biologist's viewpoint. Permit me, therefore, to lead you back to the 1920's as a starting point for our considerations.

This was the time after the first great war, a hard time as you may believe one who lived it through in impoverished Vienna. But it also was a sunset of old European culture, and a period of high intellectual intensity. At this time, a number of developments started, the significance of which became apparent only much later.

In 1926, the first German edition of Werner's *Developmental Psychology* was published, in which he introduced his organic-developmental approach. In retrospect, we may say that Werner's was one of the first programs to overcome the positivistic-mechanistic-behavioristic philosophy dominating in psychology then and even now. In biology, I advocated an "organismic" conception, presented in *Modern Theories of Development* in 1928. In brief summary, the principles of organismic biology were: "The conception of the living system as a whole in contrast to the analytical and summative points of view; the dynamic conception in contrast to static and machine-theoretical conceptions; the conception of the organism as a primary activity in contrast to the conception of its primary reactivity." The parallelism with Werner's ideas is obvious. Again, in these years Cassirer's massive volumes on *Symbolic Forms* appeared. I am afraid that few people read them in these days—and I was not among them. In the meantime, we have learned the significance of this monumental work. Piaget's first studies also fall in this period. I could go on into rather amusing detail; for example the rediscovery of Cardinal Nicholas of Cusa who, in the fifteenth century, was a sort of father figure to modern holistic and perspective philosophy; Cassirer and I brought him out independently—and in essentially identical evaluation—in 1927 and 1928. Sorokin's *Contemporary Sociological Theories* of 1928 was a vast analysis (similar, in disposition, to the much shorter *Modern Theories of Development*) of existing doctrines, establishing sociology as a science of sociocultural systems *sui generis*.

I could continue this enumeration, but the point I wish to make will have become apparent. Workers widely separated geographically, without contact with each other, and in very different fields arrived at essentially similar conceptions—sometimes to the point of almost literal coincidence of expression. In other words: developments emerging from different sources—experimental embryology, developmental psychology, cultural anthropology, neo-Kantian philosophy, sociology and others—*converged* into closely related conceptions of the organism, man and society—developments which only in recent years came to full fruition.

And this is a question not just of abstract theory and specialties in the Ivory Tower of academic science. Rather, it is part of a far wider question: that science, and a science *of* and *for* man in particular, has become deeply problematic in our days.

It is commonplace to say that the utopia of progress which has guided Western science and technology from its beginnings up till now has faltered in the modern world, when control of physical forces has led to the menace of atomic annihilation, and society has become meaningless and unhappy in the midst of plenty. The disillusionment, the realization that science is not the highway to paradise, has taken innumerable forms of expression. Let me mention only one, brilliantly expounded by a German scholar, Friedrich Wagner (1964). In a contemporary version of Thucydides' thesis (of which the author probably is unaware) he maintains that science, from Columbus and Copernicus to nuclear and cosmic physics, hydrogen bombs and space travel, essentially is a manifestation of human *hubris*, transgressing the limitations imposed by God or by man's nature, and hence inexorably leading to self-destruction. Much can be said for this view of man as sorcerer's apprentice, frivolously liberating forces that far surpass control by his intellectual and moral capacities. Nevertheless, this is romanticism no less than the romanticism of necessary and continuous progress by science and technology. Mankind was expert in making themselves miserable long before there was any science to speak of. Science can hardly be blamed for the unspeakable social conditions of the Middle Ages, the Thirty Years' War, the Spanish Inquisition and other charming episodes of history. The reason for our predicament, it seems, is not man's scientific and technological *hubris* defying divine or human law—it is man's nature itself, split into animal and something more than animal. If science, with devastating logic, has eventually led to the brink of self-negation by atomic fire, it is unrealistic to make science the villain in the play. The sanguinary course of history from its very beginnings does not reveal a better nature of man than the depravity of strategists of thermonuclear war. Rather it seems that the death instinct—to speak Freudian language—goes with man all through his history, science or no science, only its manifestations becoming more sophisticated and far wider question: that science, and a science *of* and *for* man in and scientists—half Prometheus, half lackeys to the industrial-military complex—have exacerbated the problem to the grotesque length of possible self-destruction of the species, with other problems, from the population explosion and automation to suicidal boredom in a cybernetic society, thrown into the bargain. Considering what scientists have done with the forces of nature they have conquered or released, I shudder when thinking about the latest utopia, the possible control of heredity by artificial insemination and eventually artificially manufactured genes.

Fortunately, we are not obliged to solve the human problem or give a theodicy and can focus on a smaller and more tractable question. Let us ask: What is the position of *psychology in the modern world?* By and large, an answer can be given: *Science has conquered the universe but forgotten or even actively suppressed human nature*. This is at least part of our trouble.

This thesis would deserve much broader elaboration than I can provide, going back at least to Descartes and possibly farther. Arbitrarily, I am limiting my considerations to the present century.

## Man the Robot

Let us face the fact: a large part of modern psychology is a sterile and pompous scholasticism which, with the blinders of preconceived notions or superstitions on its nose, doesn't see the obvious; which covers the triviality of its results and ideas with a preposterous language bearing no resemblance either to normal English or normal scientific theory; and which provides modern society with the techniques for the progressive stultification of mankind.

We seem to be on the horns of a dilemma. American positivist philosophy—and the same applies even more to psychology—has been said to have achieved the rare feat of being both extremely boring and frivolous in its unconcern with human issues (Kaufmann, 1957, p. 50). The famous battalions of rats working innumerable Skinner boxes have so little to tell about the human condition, our sorrows and the problems of our age. On the other hand, there are grand views of the human problem from synthesizers like Spengler, Sorokin, Toynbee, to Teilhard de Chardin and the existentialists; but they are rejected nearly unanimously by orthodox science. The basic question to modern psychology and sociology, it seems, is whether they can be *human* —concerned with the issues, temporal and eternal, of man and society; and at the same time *scientific*—true to fact and guided by that discipline of method that has developed over the past few centuries.

Psychology is characterized by a surfeit of theories ranging from neurochemistry to existentialism. Karl Bühler, in 1927, coined the phrase, "Crisis of Psychology," but even now psychology is said to be "at the crossroads" (Royce, 1965). Forty years is a rather long time for being in a crisis or at crossroads. Nevertheless, a remarkable fact seems to emerge from the conflict of contradictory theories.

Psychology, in the first half of the twentieth century, was dominated by a positivistic-mechanistic-reductionistic approach which can be epitomized as *the robot model of man.* Notwithstanding the great differences in theories such as psychoanalysis, classical and neobehaviorism, learning theory, "thinking machines" and the simulation of behavior by computers, they all shared a basic conception which served as an *a priori* framework for experimental and clinical research, theory, psychopathology, psychotherapy, etc. It is important to identify this predominant ideology.

Basic for the interpretation of animal and human behavior was the *stimulus-response scheme* or, as we may also call it, the doctrine of the *primary reactivity of the psychophysiological organism.* Behavior is response to stimuli coming from outside. This principle of reactivity entails that of *environmentalism* or other-directedness, to use Riesman's term. So far as it is not innate or instinctive, behavior is shaped by outside influences that have met the organism in the past: classical conditioning after Pavlov, instrumental conditioning after Skinner, early childhood experience after Freud, secondary reinforcements after more recent theories. Hence training, education and human life in general are essentially response to outside conditions: beginning in early childhood with toilet training and other manipulations whereby socially acceptable behavior is gratified and undesirable behavior blocked; continuing with education, which is best carried through according to Skinnerian principles of reinforcement of correct responses and by means of teaching machines; and ending in adult man in an affluent society which makes everybody happy, conditioning him, in strictly scientific manner, by the mass media to be the perfect consumer—that is, an automaton properly answering in the ways prescribed by the industrial-military-political establishment.

Philosophically, environmentalism is, of course, a latter-day version of Locke's *tabula rasa.* In intraspecific terms, it means *egalitarianism*; in interspecific, *zoomorphism* of human behavior.

Egalitarianism is one of those glories of human thought which were converted into caricature. Millennia were needed, in history, to arrive from suppression of the majority of human beings to their being handled, to an extent, as equals and brothers. Quickly, however, the ethical ideal became a scientistic dogma.

As behavior and personality essentially are shaped by conditioning in Pavlov's, Skinner's or Freud's sense, there is not much difference between human individuals, and even between pigeons, rats and monkeys on the one hand and human beings on the other. The same principles apply everywhere—and it is a good thing that they do; for this is true democracy. Hence it is only proper that what is outstanding is cut down to size; while the subnormal, abnormal, pathological and even criminal must, by touching concern and care far surpassing that for the healthy, be brought back into the flock of general uniformity. After all, when a child is asocial or fails in school, when a juvenile commits a rape, or a criminal—poor chap that he is—becomes a murderer, it's all the fault of wrong upbringing, sibling rivalry and the like.

There is, in our society, a veritable fascination with all that is sick, degenerate or substandard. The three percent of mentally retarded children in the population are in the center of public concern; the normal 97 percent must do with teachers, far too few in number, ill paid, and working under a system such that adolescents reaching university do not command their mother tongue. The same applies, with slight variations, to delinquents and criminals lovingly cared for while "senior citizens" are left to pauperism; and to every sort of scum in society which, for the reason of its degeneracy, hits the headlines.

The same principle is supposed to work the other way also. If the Russians do better in rockets or bombs, let's put a few more billion dollars into education and we shall produce a crop of young Einsteins, made to order.

The robot model or principle of reactivity further entails the *equilibrium theory* of behavior. The natural state of the organism is that of rest. Every stimulus is a disturbance of equilibrium; behavioral response, therefore, is its re-establishment; it is *homeostasis, gratification of needs* or *relaxation of tensions*. The needs are essentially biological, pre-eminently hunger and sex. Again it follows that the behavior of animals such as rats, cats and monkeys provides the necessary bases for interpretation and control of human behavior; what appears to be special in man is secondary and ultimately to be reduced to biological drives and primary needs.

Finally, behavior is basically governed by *utilitarian principles*. Maintenance of the individual and survival of the society and species are the ultimate rationale of all behavior. They are governed by the economic principle of reaching the prescribed goal with minimum expense. This applies generally, be it to a rat collecting pellets, a student collecting marks, or an adult collecting maximum salary. The story is always the same: reaching optimum psychosocial equilibrium by answering outside demands in reinforced responses.

This, in brief outline, is the robot model of man. No doubt, it covered a wide area of behavior, animal and human. It also led to a remarkable degree of theoretical unification. Machines, animals, infants and mentally sick provide adequate models for human behavior: machines because behavior is eventually to be explained in terms of machine-like structures of the nervous system; animals because of the identity of principles in animal and human behavior, and because they can be better handled; and infants because in these—as well as in pathological cases—the primary factors are better recognizable than in the normal adult.

Even more convincing than research and theory in psychology is their vast application, in contemporary life and society, for behavioral engineering. Advertisers, political parties and governments would hardly spend astronomical sums for mass persuasion and behavioral manipulation if the procedure were ineffective.

On the other hand, the limitations of robot man should be apparent. The S-R scheme discards a large part of behavior which is expression of autonomous activity: play, exploratory behavior, any form of creativity. Environmentalism is refuted by the elementary fact that not even fruit flies or Pavlovian dogs are equal. Even less can egalitarianism apply to human individuals, and zoomorphism to the comparison of subhuman and human behavior. The principle of equilibrium or tension reduction is refuted by the fact that complete relaxation of tensions—say, sensory deprivation but even simple boredom—does not lead to a beatific state of nirvana but rather to mental disturbance; in the first case, to psychosislike states, in the second to the experience of meaninglessness, sometimes culminating in existential neurosis and suicide. Juvenile delinquents who commit crime for fun, a novel psychopathology resulting from leisure, the fifty percent mental cases in the population of our hospitals—all this is proof that the scheme of robot man doesn't work. Not to mention that "culture" is beyond the utilitarian concepts—it neither guarantees mental equilibrium in their creators, nor is it of recognizable value for the survival of nations and humanity as a whole.

## Sociology of Robot Man

At this point, I expect protestations. My summary, it will be said, is an oversimplification or caricature; I am knocking down a straw man I myself have erected. For present-day psychology has corrected the excesses of early behaviorism and psychoanalysis, and is happily progressing in a broad phalanx of investigators, graduates, theses, large departments and generous grants for research.

It would require more detailed investigation to determine whether the robot scheme still dominates academic psychology.[1*] To a large extent, it certainly does as survey of current research and literature would easily show. Penetrant criticism has come forward (e.g., Allport, 1955; Sorokin, 1956; Koestler, 1964; but as a rule, it has been bypassed rather than answered, frequently by the simple expedient of ignoring it. By and large, the prevailing attitude seems to be well epitomized in a critique of Koestler's *Act of Creation* by one of our leading psychologists (Miller, 1964). Koestler, it will be remembered, argues against predominating conceptions in psychology and for "creative" principles, much in the spirit of "progressive" psychologists like G. Allport, Werner, Goldstein and others. The critic does not—and presumably cannot—refute Koestler's argument. Instead he states: "Koestler writes as though it were still in the 1930s and behaviorism were in its prime. In 1964 most psychologists who still work in this tradition have introduced hypothetical mechanisms to mediate between stimulus and response," hence Koestler's is a "misrepresentation" of current psychology justly to be dismissed. As Koestler has rather diligently searched the literature up to 1960 or so and no major revolution has occurred since, the fairness of the judgment may be questioned. But, more important, the statement seems clearly to define the point. Hypothetical mechanisms, intervening variables, auxiliary factors have been introduced—*without changing the basic concepts or general outlook.* But what we need—not only in academic psychology but even more pressingly in modern life, *which is manipulated by robot psychologists* in the mass media, in advertising and politics—what we need are not some new hypothetical mechanisms better to explain peculiarities in the behavior of the laboratory rat; we need a *new conception of man.*

More important than academic niceties is the fact that psychol-

* **1** Numbers refer to Notes, pp. 116–32.

ogy today is a *social force* of the first order, molding man's self-image and directing society.[2]

The image of man as robot is a projection into science of the *Zeitgeist* of the period, as, in the last resort, all basic theoretical notions are. Man as a machine that can be programmed; all those machines equal like automobiles coming from the assembly line; equilibrium or comfort as ultimate value; behavior as a business transaction with minimum expense and maximum gain—this is a perfect expression of the philosophy of commercial society. Stimulus-response, input-output, producer-consumer are all the same concepts, only expressed in different terms. The basic notions of conventional psychology are indeed identical with the "pecuniary philosophy" (Henry, 1963) of commercialism. In the advertisers' philosophy, there is a "brain box"—the black box of psychologists—which must be stuffed full with the advertiser's slogans to the exclusion of others; in "pecuniary logic," reality and truth are replaced by wishful thinking and conditioning by advertising art; and, of course, people are manipulated as they deserve, that is, as overgrown Skinner rats.

I don't care a jot whether and to what extent professors A, B or C have modified Watson, Hull and Freud, and have replaced their blunt statements by more qualified and sophisticated circumlocutions. I do care a lot that the spirit still is all-pervading in our society and, even more, seems necessary to keep it going: reducing man to the lower levels of his animal nature, manipulating him into a feeble-minded automaton of consumption or a marionette of political power, systematically stultifying him by a perverse system of education; in short, dehumanizing him ever further by means of a sophisticated psychological technology. The effects of this manipulation we see everywhere: in the unspeakable vulgarity of popular culture; in unbearable children and teenagers who do not know their mother tongue when entering college but are glued to the television screen for five hours a day, and find no better outlet than drug addiction, premature pregnancies or delinquency; in a drab society which in the midst of idiotic superficialities must go begging for rudiments of care for the sick or aged, or for those things of culture every poor Balkan nation can afford, and which, through its meaningless rat race, fills thousands of mental hospitals; in politics which has converted Jeffersonian democracy into a manipulated herd of cattle. Obviously, this—and much more—was not caused by modern science but has deeper social and historical roots. But, equally true, the behavior boys have made the system efficient, in the same way the atom boys provided for the ultimate horrors of modern war.

It is well to realize both the power and the limits of manipulating psychology and behavioral engineering. If you manipulate a dog according to Pavlov, a cat according to Thorndike, or a rat according to Skinner, you will obtain the results described by these authors. That is, you select, out of their behavioral repertoire, such responses as may be controlled by punishment or reward, you *make* the animals into stimulus-response machines or robots. The same, of course, is true of humans. Any well-conducted campaign—say, the last Christmas sale of war toys—is as neat a piece of behavioral experimentation as any in the laboratory. Modern psychology has all tricks to turn human beings into subhuman automata, or into a mob screaming for destruction of a supposed enemy or even of themselves; it is just a question of routine techniques used by any car dealer or television advertiser.

However, in so doing, you de-rattisize rats and de-humanize humans. That is, you remove everything that may interest a rat in its natural habitat, or you bring a cat into a "surrealistic universe" (Koestler) such as Thorndike's device. We don't know what a rat feels in a Skinner box, and what consequences the experiment has for its mental well-being. Considering that rats are chosen as laboratory animals for their stupid docility, these may be slight, while Thorndike's cats got furious, and frantically tried to get out. So far as humans are concerned, we, too, are put into a surrealistic universe—full of gadgets but devoid of interests (except the primitive ones of food, sex and shelter)—just as Thorndike's cats found only levers and keys in otherwise terrifying surroundings. If rats in the experiments, as has been said (Howarth, 1954), are handled by a giant high as a tower to them, and have to comply with his whims, we similarly have to conform to a leviathan-like society, handling us in similar ways. As the mental capacities of man are somewhat higher than those of rats, the results of deprivation, suppression of natural potentialities, and reduction to automaton-like response are more drastic; and you have what is very properly called the rat race of modern life, meaninglessness, existentialism, beatniks, neuroses and the rest.

Because we *treat* human beings after the model of Skinner rats, because we turn them even more into robots, we have all the problems from "Johnny can't read" to juvenile delinquency to the retirement neurosis of the successful businessman and the menace of leisure in cybernetic society.

Thus we urgently need a *science of mass persuasion* (Maloney, 1964), both for the manipulators seeking more effective ways and for the manipulated to guard against them. For here is the rub. Mass persuasion is, of course, one of the oldest human arts, from the sophists of Athens, the rhetoric of Aristotle and the medieval *trivium* to Hitler's famous manual. But, so long as it was art, its effects remained capricious and unpredictable, as well as limited in space and time. Rebellion was possible even against the most powerful dictator; as a matter of historical fact, dictators usually came to a bad end. This was basically changed when mass persuasion became scientific, using psychological mechanisms and techniques. Then its power, because not imposed from outside but internalized, became unlimited and nearly impregnable; aided by mass media whose barrage has no limits in space and is nearly continuous in time. This—besides nuclear weapons—is the great discovery of our age: the power of modeling men into automata "buying" everything from toothpaste and Beatles to presidents, atomic war and self-destruction.

## Anthropomorphism and Zoomorphism

Psychology in the past fifty years was a fight against what has been called the *anthropomorphic fallacy,* that is, imputing to animals human sentiments and capabilities. But it was forgotten that there equally is a *zoomorphic fallacy,* canceling any difference between animal and man. Arthur Koestler has expressed this even more nicely, saying that, "for the anthropomorphic view of the rat, American psychology has traded in a rattomorphic view of man" (1964, p. 560).

Incidentally, the choice of the rat as a model for human behavior has a sinister irony of which the creators of behaviorism were unaware. Of course, they chose the rat as an easily breeding, docile and rather stupid animal which for these very reasons was suitable for all sorts of manipulation. What they did not know, and what was discovered only recently, is that the rat *en masse* is one of the cruelest and most belligerent beasts in existence—offering itself in this respect as an excellent model for the fratricidal strivings in *Homo sapiens.* Details may be found in Lorenz's (1966) book. In brief, rats form superfamilies united by descent and nest odor, and wage veritable battles up to mutual destruction if two such herds happen to encounter or to compete for territory. One is vividly reminded of family feuds like the Montagues and Capulets in Renaissance Italy, or else of the power blocks of our times—the difference being that it is a matter of physical nest odor in rats, and symbolic nest odor in man.[3]

It should be noticed that zoomorphism is a vice of American psychology, not of European ethology. Programmatically, the ethologist investigates animal behavior in its specificity. Not surprisingly, he finds only too much we share with our animal ancestors and cousins. But, by the same token, he will be prepared to recognize what is specific of *Homo sapiens* in comparison to other species, just as he emphasizes behavioral differences of species of fish or geese. Thus Lorenz probes deeply into the biological roots of human aggression and its parallels among animals while acknowledging the "unique position of man," "cultural tradition," etc.

It is the zoomorphic or rattomorphic fallacy—the expressed or implicit contention that there is no essential difference between rat and man—which makes American psychology so profoundly disturbing. That there is a thing called *human culture* with its myriads of manifestations, and that there is nothing of the sort in pigeons and monkeys, is an observed fact—just as that pigeons and monkeys happen to have backbones, and sea urchins and earthworms have not. I do not worry that the masses prefer television to Telemann, boxing to Bach. So they always did and presumably will ever do. But when the intellectual élite, the thinkers and leaders, see in man nothing but an overgrown rat—and manipulate him accordingly and successfully—then it is time to be alarmed. A low in the spiritual barometer has been reached which can only predict hurricane and impending disaster.

In the end, the effects of modern psychotechniques and behavioral engineering amount to *functional decerebralization,* that is, exclusion of higher cerebral centers and mental faculties—almost as efficiently as if these were removed by surgical operation. Then the behavior of rats, cats and the mentally defective can indeed serve as model of "human behavior." Not even the threat of atomic annihilation can change the ways of a manipulated humanity, which are almost as strongly ingrained as the instinctive urge of a herd of lemmings, leading them irresistibly into self-destruction. In "mentalistic" terms, the same may be termed *menticide* (Meerloo, 1954; von Bertalanffy, 1960c); a procedure actually more efficient and irrevocable than clumsy attempts at genocide. For, thanks to the regenerative powers of nature, genocide, at least up till now, has proved to be rather ineffective. Extermination of millions did not destroy the races and peoples concerned but was quickly followed by replacement and even population explosion. Menticide, in contrast, is highly successful and irreversible. If a population is manipulated in the right ways, it cannot transmit, to coming generations, values and freedom it has lost itself; and this is precisely what psychological manipulation aims at and has widely achieved.

It has turned out, however, that the great behavioral experiment has failed. The hypothesis was that, given material well-being, society manipulated according to scientific principles would arrive at the greatest happiness of the greatest number. The experiment was carried out as well as large-scale social experiments permit. In view of the necessity of the "war against poverty" at home and chronic or rampant starvation in large parts of the globe, it cannot be claimed that the twentieth century has solved the social problem at large; but it did solve it in that wide sector of the Western world known as affluent society. Hence the condition of the experiment was given; and this part of humanity was treated according to "scientific" principles: permissive education; conditioning, according to the best methods of manipulative psychology, for the perfect consumer; relaxation of sexual norms to avoid formation of complexes; and so forth. As a matter of fact, no society was ever so much concerned with its own mental health, and has tried so hard to employ "scientific" principles in all ways of life. Hence, affluent society should have reached a state of psychosocial bliss never attained in the times of poverty, sexual taboos, medieval education, ignorance of the scientific principles of human behavior, and of all sorts of "mentalistic nonsense."

The outcome, unfortunately, contradicted expectation. Precisely in affluent society, with gratification of biological needs, reduction of tensions, education and conditioning with scientific techniques, there was an unprecedented increase in mental illness, juvenile delinquency, crime not for want but for fun, the serious problem of leisure in an automated society, and the appearance of new forms of mental disorder diagnosed as existential disease, malignant boredom, suicidal retirement neurosis and the like—in fact, all symptoms of a sick society.

The "image of man" is not a theoretical question; it is a question of preservation of man as *human.* One need not be a mystic like Teilhard de Chardin to see in evolution the evolution of mind. With robot psychology and technology, we have partly succeeded in the *reversal* of the evolutionary trend.

As war, according to a famous dictum, is too important to be left to generals, psychology is too important to be left to psychologists. Once more, we have to find a new conception of man. There is something basically wrong; and we must find out what it is or perish.

## Toward a New Image of Man

In the past twenty years or so, dissatisfaction with the mechanistic attitude has led to a multitude of developments in psychology which are different in content but which agree in the rejection of the robot model of man. Werner's organismic-developmental approach was one of the first and foremost among these trends. Other names and currents come easily to mind: Gordon Allport, the Bühlers, Piaget, Goldstein, Maslow, Schachtel, J. Bruner, the New Look in perception, the emphasis on exploratory behavior and creativity, neo-Freudians such as Rogers and the ego psychologists, Sorokin in sociology, phenomenological and existentialist approaches, and others. The field is large, my time and competence limited; so I again must resort to oversimplification.

I believe that there are certain principles in common in an emerging psychology of man or, as we should rather say, in a new science of man or general anthropology, because this will obviously be an interdisciplinary enterprise including biology, psychiatry, sociology, linguistics, economics, the arts and other fields. The key words of a new psychology, I propose, are *symbolism* and *system*. Somewhat more precisely: we have to define what is specific of human behavior and psychology; this is possible in terms of man's symbolic activities. And against the robot model of the primary reactivity of the organism a new conception emerges which, in psychological language, can be termed that of man as an active personality system. I arrived at these notions long ago from my biological background. They seem now to become central in various recent developments in psychology. I shall deal with the questions of "symbolism" first, and those of "system" later.

## Anthropogenesis

The biological foundations of the evolution of man have been discussed in an enormous literature, and I have expressed my opinions on several occasions. So I shall limit myself to a few remarks. Among the major anatomical and physiological presuppositions of anthropogenesis are the increase of brain size; erect posture and gait; lack of specialization and preservation of primitive characteristics such as the five-fingered hand of primates (as contrasted to special adaptations in two- and one-hoofed ungulates, carnivores, sea mammals, etc.), which made the hand a precious potential tool to "handle" things; preservation of pronation and supination of the forelimb as opposed to the fixation of the pronate position of radius and ulna in other mammalian orders; forward shift of the eye axes making possible binocular vision and depth perception; relative reduction of denture compared, e.g., to anthropoids, leading to subordination of the facial cranium to the brain case; a deep-reaching change of the hormonal balance leading to postponement of puberty and retardation of human development, providing for a long learning period and distinguishing the human growth curve from others by its bipartite course and appearance of an "adolescent spurt" of growth; man's being the unique case of a "secondary nidicolous" species, that is one born with high cerebralization and after long gestation which would anatomically qualify as a nidifugous animal, but which is behaviorally helpless and hence for a long time under maternal care.

These and other features of the biology of man have been elaborated and variously emphasized by numerous writers. One is, however, impressed by the fact that apparently no characteristic can be singled out as "the" factor responsible for man's becoming human. For example, the increase in brain size obviously is fundamental but it would have been of little value without, e.g., the prehensile hand and the hormonally controlled retardation to make use of it. Erect gait preceded increase of brain size, as is emphasized in modern anthropogeny by the distinction of an *erectus* prior to the *sapiens* phase of humans. It literally elevates a being above its creeping and running brethren and makes it a born commander and explorer, but only if other conditions are given: kangaroos and squirrels also are bipeds and at least partly "erected" but this did not result in noticeable evolution of brain and intelligence. "World-openness" (see below) presupposes lack of specialized instincts which tend to narrow down the world into one of innumerable Uexküllian ambients (*Umwelten*), but this would make the species highly vulnerable if not compensated for in other ways. Only a garrulous species with the necessary anatomical equipment can arrive at a vocal communication system, but much has to be added to chattering and howling to make a language. And so forth. Speaking in terms of genetics and evolution, there is reason to ponder how all this and more was fitted together by way of stepwise random mutations.

The paleontological record permits establishment of man's ancestry almost as well as that of horses or titanotheres. By their very nature, however, bones and teeth are unilluminating in many respects. And, even if we encountered a live Australopithecus, Pithecanthropus, Sinanthropus, or Heidelberg man, his appearance would leave unanswered many features which, in fact, are lost in the mist of times.

In a similar way, we can readily indicate quite a few necessary, although by no means sufficient, behavioral conditions in anthropogenesis. Among these, probably the poverty of innate behavioral mechanisms and lack of specialized instincts should be ranked first. This is the behavioral counterpart of the lack of anatomical adaptations; it entails the predominance, in man, of learned over innate behavior. Man's "biological helplessness" at the same time makes him "open to the world." Animals are safe in the cocoon of their ambient or *Umwelt* (von Uexküll), which is woven from their sensory equipment and innate reactions. The rest of the world does not exist for the particular species. Here, however, is a being lacking such cocoon but endowed with unique brain power. Therefore, any part of the world, from galaxies inaccessible to direct perception and biologically irrelevant, down to equally inaccessible and biologically nonexistent atoms, can become an object of "interest" to man. He invents accessory sense organs to explore them, and learns behavior to cope with them. Precisely the lack of organic and instinctual adaptation makes him capable of conquering the whole planet, and regions beyond.

Further behavioral prerequisites come easily to mind. In order to develop his self-created *Umwelt*—called human culture—man must be a social animal. Only then, communication becomes a biological necessity. If man did not have social drives, there would be no human society. With Hobbes's *bellum omnium contra omnes* as primeval human condition, society, matrimony and other institutions could not have arisen. But this socialization must not go so far as to be instinctively fixed, as in insect societies which in many respects—smoothness of the social arrangement, lack of conflicts, of social problems, etc.—far surpass human societies.

It is important to inventory man's innate or instinctive equipment and its consequences in human behavior. This leads to problems such as intraspecific aggression, with its manifestations in human cruelty, war, possible self-destruction and so forth. Based on his incomparable experience, Lorenz (1966) has profoundly discussed this problem, and I would be ill advised to emulate him. At the same time, it appears that human aggression on the grand scale always has symbolic roots (see p. 32).

Vocal abilities appear prerequisite for language in the human sense (although, of course, man is by no means lacking in nonverbal languages). To develop them, creative abilities are necessary. Although monkeys and apes are noisy animals, they seem to lack them; Langer (1948, p. 85) has made the point that apes did not develop a language because they don't babble as babies.

All this could be discussed at length. We, however, shall limit our considerations to one single aspect: *the basic fact in anthropogenesis is the evolution of symbolism.*

Without this unique characteristic, any number of biological and behavioral developments would not have been sufficient to make man human.

## Outline of a Theory of Symbolism

Apart from satisfaction of biological needs man shares with animals, he lives in a universe not of things but of symbols. Whatever else the psychology of a monkey, a rat or a sea urchin may be, and however different their Uexküllian ambients or *Umwelten* are—their universe is one of physical things, food, obstacles, enemies and so forth. Man lives in a symbolic world of language, thought, social entities, money, science, religion, art—and the objective world around him, from trivial surroundings to books, cars, cities and bombs, is *materialization* of symbolic activities.

It may justly be questioned whether man is a rational animal. This doesn't need Freud's testimony; it is plain enough from life, society and history. But there can be no discussion that man is a symbol-making, symbol-using, symbol-dominated animal throughout. I could not summarize the problem of symbolism better than Kaplan did a few years ago:

> During the past fifty years it has become increasingly recognized that symbolic activity is among the most characteristic features of human existence and that the whole development of human culture is based upon man's capacity for transforming simple sensory material into symbolic vehicles—carriers of the finest intellectual and emotional distinctions. So important is symbolic activity in human life that one of the outstanding contemporary philosophers (Cassirer) has urged: "Instead of defining man as an *animal rationale,* we should define him as an *animal symbolicum.* By so doing we can designate his specific difference. . ." (Kaplan, 1961).

Symbolism and symbolic activities were practically ignored by psychology until a few years ago. Lately, they have become fashionable. Werner's and Kaplan's contributions are well known (1963); a review of recent literature on symbolism would have to include a considerable number of investigations. I do not propose to undertake such a survey; rather I shall outline a general theory of symbolism, not much bothering to separate my contributions and those of others (e.g., Cassirer, 1953–57; Langer, 1948; von Bertalanffy, 1956, 1965a).

Let us, first, re-emphasize the paradox of current psychology. For a long time, man naïvely took his superiority for granted and believed himself to be the center of the universe. The Scientific Revolution cut him down to size; and eventually he took to masochistically gloating about his being "nothing but" a heap of atoms, a bundle of reflex mechanisms, an aberrant ape or the like. It was ignored that scientific zoomorphism was no less unrealistic, biased and partial than naïve anthropocentrism. Consequently, behavioristic psychology had nothing to say about the "human problem," man's symbolic activities and culture; with the effect that the term "symbol" does not even appear in the index of leading psychological texts.

Psychoanalysis had much to say about "symbols," but in a rather strange fashion. To classical psychoanalysts, symbolism was "a sort of lumber-room of civilization" where the repressed and useless is stored (Rank and Sachs), "an archaic mode of thinking" (Jones), even though it is hard to understand how differential equations, symphonies or automobiles can be envisaged as particularly "archaic." Hence, by and large, psychoanalytic attempts at understanding culture remained at the level of Freud's *Leonardo da Vinci* story; forgetting that whatever Leonardo's childhood experiences or complexes may have been they had extremely little to do with Florentine painting or his engineering achievements, which are understandable only in terms of his time and its culture.

The biologist, therefore, will be wise to avoid both the anthropocentric and zoomorphic fallacies. This, presumably, is what "humanistic psychology" stands for. Let us look for some consequences of such viewpoint.

From the viewpoint of the neurologist we may say, in gross oversimplification, that three major layers of the brain are superimposed in man. The first is the old brain, the paleencephalon—the site, in humans, of primitive functions, drives, instincts, emotions, the primeval depth personality. The next is the new brain, neencephalon or cortex, evolving from reptiles to mammals, which is the organ of conscious perception and voluntary action. Finally in man certain highest centers are superimposed, especially the motoric speech region and large association areas. In some way or the other the neocortex is connected with the highest mental activities in man, especially his symbolic activities. Why the activities of certain limited brain areas are connected with conscious processes while the large majority of neural material is not, is completely unknown.

Man is characterized by the massive development of the cerebral cortex and the specific regions mentioned; while no comparable development is recognizable in the lower strata of his brain. This presumably is the reason why man's evolution is almost exclusively on the intellectual side. The ten billion neurons of the cortex made possible the progress from stone axes to airplanes and atomic bombs, and from primitive mythology to quantum theory. However, there is no corresponding development on the instinctual side. For this reason man's moral instincts have hardly improved over those of the chimpanzee.[4]

What now is the *definition of symbolism* as characteristic of man? (von Bertalanffy, 1956; 1965a). The word "symbolism" has been used in different ways, possibly useful depending on the aim of investigation. (I would even concede that a new term may be advisable to cover the definition I am giving.) I believe that three criteria jointly applied are necessary and sufficient to distinguish human symbolic behavior from animal behavior, which, in some respects, may be similar to or a precursor of it. Note that I am speaking as a biologist, seeking to distinguish man from other beings by empirical behavioral criteria—just as a taxonomist looks for differences to distinguish one species from another; my approach is not motivated by philosophical, metaphysical or theological considerations.

The first two criteria of symbolism are rather obvious and don't need much discussion. Symbols are *representative,* that is, the symbol stands in one way or the other for the thing symbolized. Furthermore, symbols are *transmitted by tradition,* i.e., by learning processes of the individual, in contrast to innate instincts. The third criterion I find necessary I call *freely created.* This may not be the most felicitous expression but the meaning should be clear. In conditioning, the connection between signal and thing signaled is imposed from outside. For example, Pavlov's bell means food because the sound of the bell was followed by food as the experimenter has arranged it. Or the flame, visually perceived, warns the child or kitten of the fire because he has burned himself in the first instance. The same characteristic applies to instrumental conditioning, Freudian childhood experience, etc. In contrast, there is *no biologically enforced connection between symbol and thing signified.* It would indeed be bad if the significance of red vs. green light would have to be learned by conditioning—that is, by first crashing into another car and so learning an avoidance response. Similarly, there is no biological reason why a certain thing should be called dog, *Hund, chien, cane* and so forth, according to the language in question. In this sense, symbols are *freely chosen.*

This does not mean that the prospective symbol may not have something in common with the original, or that there is no biological reason or psychological motivation in the choice of linguistic and other symbols. Werner and his associates (Werner and Kaplan, 1963; and other work) have shown the importance of "physiognomic" characteristics in symbol formation. The onomatopoetic roots of language have been widely discussed. Certain primeval words like "mamma"—and the fact that the word for "mother," in nearly all languages irrespective of their structure, begins with an "m" (personal communication of the late Prof. Kluckhohn)—indicate that they originate from a sound connected with the smacking of the baby on the mother's breast (cf. Jakobson, 1960).

The role of expressive outcry, mimesis in words and related factors in verbalization has been widely discussed in linguistics; Cassirer's work provides ample discussion of at least the older part of literature. Nevertheless, it will be agreed that the process is not at the level of biological conditioning, classical by contiguity or instrumental by reinforcement. The connection between word (or symbol) and object is not "biologically enforced from outside," but "meaning" is given to a symbol. For example, in well-known experiments by Köhler, a roundish figure was given the name "maluma" by the experimental subjects, a spiky one the name of "takete." This shows "physiognomic" similarity between figure and name attached, but has nothing to do with biological conditioning. There are "physiognomic" characteristics and a sort of isomorphy between visual image and "word"; therefore, the choice is not arbitrary. That these new "words" are affixed to structures not previously named is of course facilitated by the linguistic habits possessed by man since times immemorial. But our criterion still stands and is verified: there is no conditioning, reinforcement, etc., involved in the connection between figure and name; the connection is not imposed from outside but is established by a "creative" act on the basis of giving "meaning" to the word-symbol standing in for the thing. This creative element beyond biological conditioning is touchingly revealed in episodes such as Helen Keller's story of how she first grasped the meaning of words, the connection of symbol (in this case, in a touch language) and thing signified. The experience of awe must have been even profounder when man first discovered that a connection between freely produced signs (symbols) and things can be made.

Of course, in "verbal behavior" (Skinner, 1957) within a linguistically full-grown society the conventional pattern of operant behavior and reinforcement plays a large role. Nevertheless, as Chomsky (1959) has emphasized in his critique of Skinner's book, learning by "meaning" or "understanding" is essentially different from and cannot be reduced to reinforcement. In Skinner's scheme, there is no place for a sentence's being "true" (i.e., corresponding in some way to "fact"); one sentence is as good as the other, presupposing it is sufficiently reinforced. This, alas, is correct for manipulating psychology, the conditioning of the human animal through mores, ingrained metaphysics and prejudices, mass media and the like. It leaves completely unexplained that there is something like a search for "objective truth" (independent of and frequently contradicting reinforcement and animal gratification), that there is "meaning" beyond conditioned response to word stimuli, that the latter form grammatical patterns according to laws of symbolic systems, and so on. It appears correct to ask (as Chomsky implies) why there is language in the human sense at all, clearly distinguished by unique properties from animal behavior and communication, if "verbal behavior" is based upon principles germane to man and rat, and nothing else or beyond.

The criterion "biologically imposed" is connected with that of "biological usefulness." Obviously, nonsymbolic behavior is, as a rule, self-preserving and species-preserving, as in learning behavior, innate responses and communications, etc.; even though, in the creation of tensions, play, exploratory behavior it is not simply homeostatic but expression of "autonomous activity" of the organism. By and large (although with exceptions), biologically disadvantageous behavior will be quickly eliminated by selection. In contrast, symbolic behavior is not only creative in its roots ("autonomy" at a higher level), it also far transcends biological advantage. As has already been said, the biological and adaptive value of just the highest, symbolic and cultural activities is questionable; and in suicide, war, etc., biological values are sacrificed to symbolic ones. This is the biological background of the antithesis of "nature" and "culture." The symbolic world of culture is basically un-nature, far transcending and often negating biological nature, drives, usefulness, and adaptation.

These three criteria taken together, I have satisfied myself, are necessary and sufficient [5] to distinguish human symbolism from animal behavior which, in one way or the other, may be compared with it; for example, signals in conditioned reaction, schemata in instinct, communication between animals, the so-called language of bees, the beginnings of tradition in the teaching of parent animals to their young, and so forth. Analysis shows in any of such cases that one or the other of the criteria indicated is missing. The same applies to aberrant cases in humans: When, for example, a schizophrenic invents fancy names for things, they do not qualify as symbols or language. The criteria of "free creation" and "representation" are given, but not that of "tradition," so long as the schizophrenic's utterances remain idiosyncratic, as they do in his autistic and chaotic experience. When, however, the neologism (in the broadest sense of the word), fitting into a consistent world experience, is accepted, it becomes part of the symbolic universe; as is the case all the time, from "juvenile" and other slang becoming part of the vernacular to the invention of new mathematics, physics and so on.

It should perhaps be remembered that the concepts, symbolism and language overlap but do not coincide. There is language which is non-symbolic; following K. Bühler's proposal (1934), language as "representation," "expression" and "appeal" (*Darstellung, Ausdruck, Auslösung*) may be distinguished. Only the first is symbolic; the other two (e.g., expressive or warning cries of animals) need not be, although they may be in human communication. On the other hand, there is of course an enormous field of non-linguistic symbolism. In consideration of animal languages, of the broader connotation of symbolism compared to language, and of the probable roots of representative language in deeper layers of symbolism (such as myth), modern observers have arrived at considering symbolism rather than language as the specifically human achievement. This conclusion is confirmed by the fact that symbolic activities (as defined above) are not found in animals (anthropoids included) although, of course, precursors and preparatory stages are. As regards primates, the best observers sometimes express this by speaking of the "aphasia" or "mutism" of chimpanzees; this is connected with the lack of the motoric speech center in the frontal lobe which appears only in man (Rensch, 1958) (on animal languages, cf. the monumental work by Kainz, 1961).

This is generally agreed by biologists (e.g., J. Huxley, Dobzhansky, von Bertalanffy), primatologists (Yerkes), neurophysiologists (Luria; "secondary signal system" in Pavlovian terminology), psychiatrists (Goldstein, Arieti, Kubie, Hacker), philosophers (Cassirer, Langer), etc. That American psychology, up to very recent years, failed to understand, recognize and explore this basic characteristic and distinction of human behavior is one of the consequences of the zoomorphic fallacy and inappropriate reductionism.

The enormous range of symbols and symbolic activities further requires classification. Obviously there are two major realms. One class is concerned with communication of *cognitional information.* The main example is, of course, language; more precisely, language as representation or *Darstellung* according to K. Bühler. Its fundamental characteristic is its discursive character; hence we may speak of a realm of *discursive* symbolism.

On the other hand there is an enormous field of non-discursive symbolism carrying information not of the cognitive but of another kind: from status symbols like a Cadillac or a flag to lyrical poems, to music, to myth and religion and many other things. It seems that as a rule these are concerned with communication not of *facts* but of *values* (von Bertalanffy, 1965a). We may also speak of communication of *emotional information*—a kind of information which is not covered by information theory and cannot be expressed by bits or yes-or-no decisions in Boolean algebra. Nevertheless there it is: a Cadillac or national anthem gives information about social status or patriotic emotions just as the word "apple" informs about the implied properties of a certain thing. We may call, tentatively, the class of nondiscursive symbols *experiential.*

The consequences of man's symbolic activities are enormous; let us attempt a brief outline. The first consequence is obvious. Phylogenetic evolution based on hereditary changes is supplanted by history based on the tradition of symbols. This, of course, makes for the tremendous acceleration of happenings in human history as compared to the geological time scale of evolution.

Second, actual trial and error is replaced by reasoning, i.e., trial and error in conceptual symbols. Symbolic processes substitute experimental actions: trial and error not in action but in thought.

Third, symbolism makes true or Aristotelian purposiveness possible. The future goal is anticipated in its symbolic image and so may determine present action.

Fourth, the symbolic universes created by man gain autonomy or, as it were, a life of their own. Symbol systems, so to speak, are self-propelling. They therefore have an autonomy or inner logic of development. Myth, Renaissance painting from Giotto to Titian, music from Bach to Richard Strauss, physics from Galileo to Bohr, the British Empire, or the evolution of Indo-Germanic languages—they all follow their respective immanent laws, which are not psychological laws that characterize mental processes in their creators.

This is the reason why, by and large and neglecting transitions, we find three great realms or levels in the observed world: inanimate nature, living systems, and the symbolic universe (culture, Hegel's objective mind, T. de Chardin's noosphere, Sorokin's meaningful superorganic realm, etc.), each having its characteristic immanent laws.

Of course, distinction does not mean absolute gaps, but rather emergence from lower to higher level. In these times of molecular biology, it is hardly necessary to point at intermediates between nonliving and living, although the cell does remain the simplest system known which exhibits the full repertoire of life functions. On more familiar grounds, we have rather good series leading from amphibia to reptiles and mammals; nevertheless these classes make good sense. Similarly, we would negate developmental psychology, both in Werner's and Piaget's sense, when claiming an unbridgeable gap between biology and symbolism, biosphere and noosphere, or whatever expression we choose. But just in order to look for development and evolution, precursors, transitions, ancestry and so forth, we must first put our concepts in order and elaborate what is specific of each.

The autonomous laws of certain symbolic universes—those of discursive symbols—lead to a fifth consequence. The system wins algorithmic properties. An algorithm is a system of symbols, connected according to pre-established rules. One may take elementary algebra or any kind of mathematics as example, but also vernacular and technical languages. Given a suitable set of symbols, i.e., a *vocabulary*, and given suitable rules of the game, a *grammar*, symbols can be handled as tokens of the things they represent. Then, to quote the famous dictum of Heinrich Hertz, "the consequences of the images will be the images of the consequences." In somewhat different terms, the algorithmic system becomes a calculating machine, as conversely every calculating machine is materialization of an algorithm. Suitable data being fed in, the machine runs according to pre-established rules, and eventually a result drops out which was unforeseeable to the individual mind with its limited capacities. This is the essence of mathematical reasoning, prediction in science and control of nature in technology.

Sixth, there are, however, gloomy aspects of symbolic universes. The conceptual anticipation of the future which allows for true purposiveness at the same time creates anxiety, fear of future and death, unknown to animals.

Owing to their immanent dynamics or laws, symbolic systems may become more potent than man, their creator. Then symbolic entities—status, nation, society, party, what have you—may govern man and human behavior more strongly than biological reality or organismic drives. This is the basis of the most sublime achievements of man; it is also the cause of all the follies of human history. Thermonuclear bombs are not only the ultimate weapon but the ultimate of symbolisms run wild in science, technology and politics.

If a clash arises between biological drives and symbolic values, or between contradicting symbolic worlds, then, for the individual, the situation of neurosis arises. Neurosis is not simply suppression of "instincts" or biological needs, as Freud presumed; modern analysts recognize the essential role of symbolism (Kubie, 1953; Hacker, 1965).

Essentially the same applies to societies. As has already been said, conflicts and wars are not at the biological level of survival and struggle for existence; they are a clash between ideologies or symbolic worlds. More precisely, they are an outcome of verbal magic hypostatizing words—nationalism, free enterprise, communism, confessional dogma or whatever else, which at best mirror certain aspects of reality, and at worst are completely unrealistic —into specious realities, by the well-known and pernicious process of reification of concepts.

"Thus man has to pay for the uniqueness that distinguishes him from other beings. The tree of knowledge is the tree of death" (von Bertalanffy, 1956).

Thus symbolism is the very basis of human nature and the human predicament. *All* specifically human behavior, achievement, work and suffering can be expressed in terms of symbolic activities.

To make it a holy Seven, let us add what is possibly the profoundest result of symbolism. It creates the "I" and the "world." Immediate experience, such as perceptions, feelings, acts of will, is momentary—dominating consciousness at one moment and gone the next. The past, in the experience of animals, consists of traces left from conditions that influence subsequent behavior, at the most of vague after-images of past perceptions. Only with symbolism an organized "universe" arises. Only denominating symbols make perceived stimulus-gestalten into persistent objects. Only then do past and future exist in their symbolic stand-ins, thereby becoming manageable. In this way, the past becomes part of the organized universe; and the future, the not-yet-experienced, can be anticipated by way of its symbolic stand-ins, and so can determine present behavior. Symbolism makes for the *consistency* of the universe: *Was in schwankender Erscheinung schwebt, befestiget in dauernden Gedanken* (Goethe).

By means of symbols and naming, things outside, people

around and the experiencing self—the It, Thou, and I—differentiate from the stream of experience; the *ego barrier* is established. This process can be followed in the individual development of the child; in the anthropological development from myth to "objective" knowledge; in its partial reversal in psychopathology. From a syncretic stage (Werner) [6] or state of adualism (Piaget) and passing mythical and magical worlds, eventually the separation of world and self is established (cf. for example Werner, 1957; Piaget, 1959; Cassirer, 1953-57; von Bertalanffy, 1964a, 1966a; Arieti, 1965).[7]

## Some Thoughts on the Evolution of Symbolism

As already said, the distinction of animal and symbolic behavior does not mean that they are separated by an empty gap. As there are intermediates between nonliving and living nature, so we also have to seek for the evolution of symbolism. By and large, the notion of emergence appears to be correct: each level of the universe—atom, molecule, cell, organism, society, symbolic universes (with any number of interpolated levels)—has its characteristic properties and laws which cannot be simply derived from or reduced to those of the respectively lower level; in every plane there is also a gradation from lower to higher, and we can understand it, not by reduction pure and simple, but by adequate expansion of our conceptual schemes.

Concept formation and symbol formation are problems for the psychologist. However, the biologist is entitled to ask how this remarkable and unique feature of *Homo sapiens* has evolved. The answer lies somewhere in the 500,000 years separating Heidelberg man from us, and inferences drawn from developmental psychology, cultural anthropology and psychopathology are necessarily speculative. No ready-made answer is available, but some considerations may be offered.

As in all evolutionary problems, one has to be careful to distinguish parallel development and true ancestry. The problem is the familiar one of analogy and convergence. Functional equivalents may evolve independently, such as wings in insects, birds and bats, or camera eyes in vertebrates and molluscs; more to the point, they may evolve at different levels of evolution. The shells of certain unicellular foraminifera do look like miniature ammonites; in marsupials and placental mammals surprisingly similar forms have evolved.

Similar considerations apply to the problem under consideration. Strikingly resembling behavior patterns often appear at the three major levels, that of innate behavioral mechanisms, of learned reactions, and of symbolic activities. There is, for example, little difference between many rituals in animals and man. A fish or bird "showing off" by exhibiting its colors, going through a series of menacing postures and gestures, etc., indeed does the same as the owner of a new Cadillac running it 90 m.p.h. Glitter and menace are understood by both fish and man. We also shall not err in saying that motivation—drive or "primary process" in psychoanalytic parlance—is the same: showing oneself as big, powerful, virile and the like. But of course, Cadillacs did not evolve from animal coloration or plumage. It is essentially the same when Skinner stated that certain results of instrumental conditioning give rise to "superstitious behavior" in pigeons, and Henry (1964) ridiculed him for the naïveté of such comparison. For rain dances and similar rituals of course are based on an enormous symbolic structure of religion, beliefs, social organization and so forth.

Here, it would appear, we have the problem in a nutshell. Symbolic behavior, the "secondary process," cannot be "reduced" or "resolved into" primary process, innate action schemes or simple learning processes. On the other hand, primary motivation goes right through all behavioral levels. Using an example already mentioned: Human warfare cannot be reduced to man's aggressive drive; war and so-called essential aggression in the great scourges of mankind from Tamerlane to contemporaries presuppose not only bloodthirsty and belligerent instincts but an elaborate symbolic framework, an ideology (von Bertalanffy, 1958);

and modern conflicts, rather than following blind aggression, are results of ice-cold calculation (or so it is claimed; we should not forget fixed ideas and outright schizophrenic thinking in international politics). But, by the same token, war would be biologically impossible except for the instinctual possibility of intraspecific aggression (Lorenz, 1966). Furthermore, "killer" species also have inbuilt mechanisms inhibiting intraspecific murder, e.g., the well-known example of the wolf who, when vanquished in combat, presents his enemy his weakest part for the kill—and just by doing so, evokes a "chivalrous" instinct inhibiting the victor's final snap. In contrast, unarmed species like meek pigeons, which under normal circumstances would not hurt each other, ruthlessly kill the vanquished under artificial conditions of crowding because of the lack of inhibitory mechanisms which did not evolve because they were unnecessary in normal wild life. This also is the danger of the man with the gun or the atom bomb; there is no instinctual inhibition to murder *en masse* by unbiological devices, while the same individual, with his natural weapons of fists and teeth, would not "hurt a fly" and even less a child.

Furthermore, the higher symbolic level or secondary process would not even be possible except on the basis of primary process, of the unconscious and its neural equivalent. Lorenz (1959) has emphasized the "ratiomorphic" character of reflex and instinct action. Even a completely unconscious process, such as size constancy in perception or grasping an object, presupposes an enormous amount of "calculation," of feedback, the play of a "neural computer" of fantastic complexity. Only a minute part of the brain's "calculations" becomes conscious or "secondary process." This "ratiomorphic" feature is the reason for the anthropomorphic error, instinctive behavior (think, for example, of wasps paralyzing caterpillars by the most delicate injection of venom near the appropriate ganglions to prepare them as food for the young) appearing "as if" it were intelligent and directed by foresight of the goal; which, of course, it is not. Contrariwise, the "ratiomorphic" structure of behavior and the brain as calculating machine are prerequisites without which secondary process, consciousness and symbolic activities would not be possible.

So here is the basic problem. The evolution of symbolism, we have said, is the fundamental problem of anthropogenesis. *All* other human achievements are minor or derived from it. For example, language: The bees have a perhaps even more perfect communication system; and there can be no dispute that insect societies work much more perfectly and smoothly than their human counterparts. Or technology, man the *Homo faber*.[8] With few exceptions—the wheel, the cracking of atoms and space flight—nature's technology surpasses that of man—to the extent that the traditional relationship between biology and technology was recently reversed: while mechanistic biology tried to explain organic functions in terms of man-made machines, the young science of bionics instead tries to imitate nature's inventions. Only in one respect, there is that *mysterium tremendum et fascinosum*: that a biologically inferior and helpless organism in the unique way of symbolic activity transcends and vanquishes nature and evolution. Symbolism, if you will, is the divine spark distinguishing the poorest specimen of true man from the most perfectly adapted animal. It is the *differentia specifica* of *Homo sapiens*, just like any taxonomic difference distinguishing one species from another. Here is a fundamental problem for psychology; the development of a *human* psychology depends on it.

As I said, I don't have—and nobody has—an easy solution. A goodly number of *precursors* can be enumerated without difficulty, material that can be used for symbolic purposes. Animal rituals as precursors of experiental symbols have already been mentioned. For the evolution of cognitive symbols, apparently some glorified gestalt perception is prerequisite: Insight or seeing things together which were previously unconnected (cf. Lorenz, 1960). Thus, any elongated object, whatever else it may be, becomes a stick to catch things with, for Köhler's ape Sultan; or it becomes a somewhat different thing in our dreams, if we are to believe Freud's interpretation. Koestler (1964) has called this bi-sociation—the bringing-together of the formerly unconnected, and has brilliantly followed it up from the ape Sultan to Archimedes and beyond. Unnecessary to say that such processes, and symbol formation in general, are largely at the unconscious level; as a rule, conscious is only the application of an already existing symbol machine or algorithm with, of course, all possible intergradations.

The *decisive* step seems to be that man, in one way or the other, made an *image* of things apt to be their representative. It is probably not so important whether this was a *graven* image —such as the paleolithic carvings of animals—or an *acoustic* image—the first word of representative language. But it was decisive that man, in some way, *dissociated* something from himself which was to stand in for something else. As the Bible very appropriately says, Adam began his career in Paradise by giving *names* to things and animals—and in this he gained domination over them. There can be hardly a doubt that the origin of symbolism is intimately connected with magic; be it *word magic*—a word gives power over the thing named; or *manipulative magic*—the clay image *is* the enemy, and he is killed when the image is transfixed with a needle. We do not know at what time precisely in human prehistory symbolic activity—creation of representations of things—originated; but it certainly was there when paleolithic hunters created the grandiose frescoes in the caves of France and Spain, no doubt for the purposes of sympathetic magic of successful hunting. Something like this must have happened in the remote past of man: some *creative act* imitating things in *image* or *sound;* this imitation followed by the progressive dissociation of three entities: the object, its visual or acoustic copy, and experiencing man himself. At first, in the state called primary adualism by Piaget and syncretic by Werner, they all were interfused; the little clay puppet or the animal depicted *was* the enemy or animal hunted; and everything done to the copy in magical practice was done to the original. Furthermore, there was no ego boundary, to use the psychiatrist's expression: world outside and self were not yet differentiated; everything, in animistic experience, was part of the soul or self. Only slowly the three elements, thing, symbol and self, differentiated out (cf. Werner and Kaplan, 1963). This is what psychologists call *progressive objectification*, found in the child's mental development and at different stages in the comparative study of cultures. Probably we must take the expression more literally than usual. It is not only objectification in the epistemological sense—distinguishing, progressively and by a host of psychological agents, perceived object and perceiving self. Rather, in the beginnings, there would have been objectification in the literal sense of *making* things or noises which could become stand-ins for some perceptual complex, subsequently could be separated from the producer, and so started the process of symbolic representation. It seems rather cogent to presume that objectification in both senses—the psycho-epistemological and the practical—were closely connected. Objectification in the epistemological sense—i.e., the differentiation of objects and subject from a primary adualistic experience—certainly was not achieved without symbolic labels or markers attached to certain complexes in perception. But this presupposed *making* things as markers or labels, be it an acoustic utterance connected with some perceptual complex, or a visual or tactile image imitating the object—the enemy, the beast hunted, the primitive deity —which again in some way was identical with the image.

I know well how insufficient all this is but this precisely shows the enormity of the problem. Indeed, here we have the *key problem* of human psychology as distinguished from the psychology of rats and cats; and I could do no more than hint at some questions and ideas.

In conclusion, symbolism is the basic invention of man, and imitative magic, in all probability, was connected with its origin. We must correctly realize the enormity of this change from the behavior of subhuman animals. It obviously took a correspondingly long time. Thus it may be easier to understand why—to judge from the tools which are the only testimony left—man apparently remained for almost a half million years at the same stage of paleolithic culture. This was the germinative period when his symbolic and linguistic universe was formed. Afterward, progress—in the high cultures arising in the river valleys of Mesopotamia, the Nile, Indus, and China—was rapid in terms of the geological time scale. And it became a torrent when (to introduce expressions I used elsewhere) "verbal magic," which proved to be ineffective, was replaced by highly efficient "magic of the algorithm," which is commonly known under the name of science—prediction and control of events by organized symbol systems.

Every theory proves itself only in its application to concrete cases. This has been attempted with respect to various problems of normal, pathological and applied psychology (cf. von Bertalanffy, 1965a). Here I choose a problem which certainly is very timely: the problem of *human values.*

## Theories of Value

There is no good in denying that our time is one of *nihilism* in Nietzsche's sense—of breakdown and devaluation of values, feeling of meaninglessness of life and human endeavor, manifesting itself in a spectrum from silly fads to crime and mental disease. Just because traditional values have become problematic, there is a frantic search for new ones and for a basis of values in general, which was alien to periods when a value system—the Christian, that of the British gentleman or of scientific perfectionism, as the case may be—was taken for granted. It seems a fair working hypothesis (Weisskopf, 1959) to distinguish three major theories of values: the *naturalistic,* the *humanistic* and the *ontological.* None of them—to anticipate the result—appears to be satisfactory.

The *naturalistic theory* of value is based on science or rather scientism. In one way or the other, the maintenance of the individual, the survival of society or species, the greatest happiness of the greatest number appear as ultimate value. Obviously, every healthy animal has an instinct or drive for survival, and in gregarious animals there are instincts for survival of the group. But, just because this is a general biological principle, it has nothing to do with specifically *human* values expressed in the traditional trinity of the true, beautiful and good, leading to human culture, science, art and religion.

To the biologist, the biological roots of human values are evident. The historian J. H. Muller has aptly expressed this:

> Since the higher values are usually given a high metaphysical or religious sanction, it is worth observing that they require no such sanction. Like the simple goods of physical well-being, they are intrinsic goods, good for their own sake. And since, as capitalized abstractions, the Good, the True, and the Beautiful are apt to seem highfalutin' in an age of business and technology, it is well to stress their homely origins. The Good is rooted in the fact that man is a social animal, naturally gregarious, whose "soul" may come from God but in any event can come simply from his relations with his fellows, and his natural desire for their esteem; his very self is a social product, or itself a society, which becomes self-conscious only as it becomes aware of other selves. The True is rooted in natural curiosity, the desire of all men to know something about whatever they are interested in, whether the workings of an engine or of a universe; the most abstruse concepts of science and philosophy grow out of simple fondness for observing the out-of-doors. The Beautiful is rooted in the esthetic sense and creative impulse common to all men, and apparent even in the hard-headed man who thinks Art is effeminate; when he admires his new tool or gadget he says, "It's a beauty." The "higher" values may be considered a simply fuller development of these natural human impulses, a fuller realization of the distinctive but natural possibilities of being a human being (1960, p. 63 f.).

Equally evident, man is an animal that creates his own environment, called culture and civilization. But this widely transcends biological usefulness, both with respect to the individual and society.

It is rather trite to say that culture and civilization cannot be accorded an unequivocal biological or survival value. By no stretch of imagination can Athenian sculpture, Renaissance painting or German music be ascribed survival value for the societies concerned—Periclean Athens, which soon succumbed to the brute Lacedemonians in the Peloponnesian War; Renaissance Italy with its political turmoil; or Germany with its awful little tyrannies in the times of Bach and Handel. So far as science is concerned it has, of course, made man the dominating animal on earth, but we have not seen the end. It is up to purely subjective sentiment whether automobiles, television, general education and so forth outweigh napalm, thermonuclear war and famine following the population explosion.

Because they are rooted in instincts of a moderately social species, the Golden Rule and similar precepts are common ground of morals among most different peoples and cultures. But, by the same token, the naturalistic proposition becomes problematic in more advanced forms of human society. Take, for example, the Hippocratic oath of the physician, indubitably a sublime moral precept. It was a most appropriate maxim in Greece in 500 B.C., that is, in a sparsely populated and cultivated country. But to what extent is it useful or even moral when modern hygiene and medicine, prolongation of life span, etc., lead to multiplication of human misery? It is Christian ethic to accept even the humblest human brother; but to what extent is the modern care for the retarded, the feeble-minded and even the criminal useful and moral, as we know, as well as any scientific fact, that the result will be deterioration of the genetic pool of the human species—breeding future generations of morons and crooks? Who tells how to apply the yardstick of preservation of life, survival and advancement of the species? American belief in progress, plumbing and democratic equality only glosses over a terrifying problem.

The interesting point about naturalistic values is that they are not human values at all, that is, not values specific of *Homo sapiens*. The so-called "highest ethical values"—"the love of the mother for her child and the man for his mate, the willingness to sacrifice one's own life for the safety of the family or tribe, and the impulse to care for the weak, the suffering, the helpless," to quote a renowned biologist (Glass, 1965)—these are no more and no less than the values of a gregarious species, equaled or even surpassed by many birds, domestic animals and wolves. Here we have again the zoomorphic fallacy. As modern ethology has elaborated in often surprising detail, *Homo sapiens* has little reason to boast about his ethical principles, which are but verbalizations of the instincts of social animals.

This has the fascinating consequence that popular value concepts are turned upside down. For example, Kant's Categorical Imperative, commonly considered as a stern moral of duty, actually is a verbalization of instinct. For it is the definition of instinct that the maxim of one's behavior can be made into universal law; and natural selection sees to it that instinct, as a rule, is preserving the species. Upgrading this into the symbolic level makes for a morality of conformity (as it historically nourished the "subject's spirit" in old Prussia and in Kant himself) but is inapplicable to human achievement. Neither Caesar's or Napoleon's, nor Christ's, St. Francis' or the Buddha's behavior could be made into universal law without disrupting society; but precisely such were the motive forces of history.

According to Puritan theory—of the New England, Kantian and Freudian variety—man's nature is essentially bad and depraved: man, the born aggressor and rapist, his savage drives precariously controlled by a supernatural factor: grace, reason, superego. It is a romantic and arrogant vision of man as a proud animal of prey, a ferocious aggressor and insatiable Don Juan, such as could be invented only by bourgeois Puritans, Königsberg and Vienna professors.

Maritain (1950, p. 185) notes a certain relationship between Lutheran and Freudian libido (and, one can add, certain of St. Augustine's concepts which were not acceptable to Roman Catholicism, much as it relied on Augustine otherwise). Concupiscence, according to Luther, is unconquerable and the original sin, making us corrupt in the very essence of our nature, and to be saved by faith alone. According to Maritain—admittedly not an impartial witness—"Luther yields to the forces of instinct, he becomes subject to the law of the flesh, following a progress which we may be permitted to remark in the series of portraits of him, the last of which are surprisingly bestial" (p. 11). Consequences of such belief are such lovely maxims of Luther's as "the work and word of God tell us clearly that woman must be used for marriage or prostitution"; "let them live, so long as they bear, they are made for that"; or "reason is the devil's whore eaten by scab and leprosy who must be trodden under foot and destroyed, she and her wisdom" (quoted in Maritain, l.c.). In fairness, it must be said that some of this is not unparalleled in Catholicism, as in St. Jerome's disapproval of bathing for virgins and advice of deliberate squalor not to distract saintly men.

The point is that *les extrèmes se touchent*: fervent supernaturalism arrives at the same bestialization of man as the zoomorphism of scientism; while this is not contained either in the original teachings of Jesus, St. Thomas' balance of man's two natures, or in objective exploration by modern science.

The ethologist, in fact, comes to a different view. Man's original nature is not so bad after all. His instinctual equipment is that of a moderately social species; that is, aggression against other species, aggression also against outside groups of his own species; but, on the other hand, tolerably strong social and monogamous instincts. Otherwise, human society and monogamy could not have developed and persisted. Lorenz (1966) correctly says that within a primitive human group—say, paleolithic people or Australian aborigines—the Ten Commandments of Mosaic law (or, if you will, Kant's Categorical Imperative) would be, and presumably were, perfectly natural and instinctual. Each little group is in a state of perpetual warfare with nature and other little groups—not very different from packs of wolves or herds of rats. But, precisely for this reason, intragroup aggression must be controlled if the group is to survive; that is, by and large, the commandments, Thou shalt not kill, not rape, not steal and so forth must be obeyed for purely biological reasons. Even more, a strong "bond"—Lorenz' expression—of comradeship, friendship, love must develop within the group—that is, very positive moral virtues.

## The Unworkable Altar

But man's original sin was precisely what the Bible says it was: eating from the tree of knowledge; that is, in modern parlance, *invention of symbolic universes*. This made man both better and worse than other species with their inbuilt drives and controls. This opened up his tremendous history from cave shelters to skyscrapers, from fetishism to Freudianism, from paleolithic painting to pop art. As already said, it did not change man's instinctual equipment. And man became the enormously dangerous beast he is precisely by the clash between instinctual and symbolic worlds, by using techniques of symbolic manipulation for aggression. Here again, the Bible is right. The first murder—Cain slaying Abel—was not a fratricide from instinctual drive; it was a fight about an unworkable altar—a symbolic artifice which would not work on Cain's part. For this reason—not because of instinctual sibling rivalry—Abel was slain by Cain. And from that moment to the present day mankind have slaughtered each other for unworkable altars; that is, for symbolic contraptions—nation, religion, dynasty, democracy, communism, whatever you want—created by man's so-called reason and lending a changing foil for that intergroup aggression which, without the symbolic superstructure, would have remained a comparatively harmless affair.

Speaking in paradox: not the law but the lawbreaker is testimony that man is more than a gregarious animal.

The other two theories of value need only brief comment. The *humanistic value theory* is centered in the notion of *self-realization* of the human individual. A most attractive post-Renaissance ideal; but then we remember that there have been societies where this was not an ideal: for example, the medieval, the orthodox Communist, the Zuni Indians after Ruth Benedict. And, without qualification, it is a two-edged notion: The great criminal or dictator may claim to be realizing his potentialities just as does the decent fellow or the creator in art and science. And there seems to be something more than self-realization of the human individual. Again borrowing a clever phrase by Koestler (1964), there certainly are more easy and comfortable ways toward self-realization than investigating nucleic acids—or, for what matter, service and sacrifice for any sort of idea.

It is this supra-individual aspect the *ontological theory* brings to the fore. But speaking of human essence is Platonism and hardly acceptable to our skeptical ways of thinking. We form a certain idealized concept of man, call it his essence—and presume that in some way it has or should have existence. This is *reification of concepts*—a very dubious procedure indeed, notwithstanding all sympathy we may harbor for existentialism and its understanding of human predicament.

How are "authentic" and "non-authentic" symbols (Tillich) to be distinguished—except by a value decision already taken? The swastika was just as authentic for many True Believers as was the cross or the stars-and-stripes. The victims of Auschwitz, of the Wars of Religion, and of Hiroshima suffered the same way, and their killers enjoyed the same good feeling of serving the "just cause." All of these—from headhunters in Borneo to Diocletian's henchmen murdering subversive Christians to Christians murdering each other for the famous iota, to the struggle between democracy, national socialism and communism—at best believed in an "authentic" ideal, and at worst were criminal tools in a brutal power struggle.

The value judgment remains subjective. If, in a key passage, Tillich (1959, p. 193) "ontologically" recognizes the *eidos* or essence in a "perfect" pine tree, I for one admire the slender pines of the Gianicolo seen from St. Peter's Square; but who has a right to despise the wretched, wind-swept, creeping pines above the tree line of the Alps? The *eidos* of pine and man is nowhere but in imagination.

In parenthesis: The origin of ontology and Platonism is not hard to understand. Symbolism is what elevates man over even the highest animals. Proud of this achievement, it is natural that man was inclined to take symbols for things. Taking symbols for things—this is not only primitive magic, it is also what in philosophical language is called realism of concepts. Plato took concepts or ideas not only as good but as superior reality; and the long struggle about the universals during the Middle Ages is, in modern terms, nothing but a dispute about what symbols are or mean.

## God Becoming Aware of Himself

So, it seems to me, little is left of conventional theories of value. It appears that there is a fourth which is tolerably free of objections. I will call it the *symbolistic theory*. It is not anthropomorphism or self-glorification to assert that there is a scale of beings and of values in nature. We do not overlook man's miserable and atrocious aspects when we say that he is somewhat more than a bedbug. The scientist can say, by quite objective criteria, that *Homo sapiens* is the highest product of terrestrial evolution. The mystic says essentially the same when claiming evolution to be God becoming aware of Himself. This is old mystical wisdom; Teilhard de Chardin has only given it a modern, and not necessarily the best expression. Only then, evolution and history are more than a tale told by an idiot, full of sound and fury, signifying nothing.

If this is so, man's achievement obviously is not in the organic lines; many animals are prettier, faster, stronger and so forth. Man's monopoly is just what we have tried to define—his symbolic activities and universes.

What is specifically human is not the "highest ethical values" of the naturalist, but the sublimation of sex into the deep understanding of matrimonial love, of the motherly tenderness of a bitch into Christian *pietà* or *caritas*, sacrifice not for the family or tribe but for things more intelligent than the tribe, small or large, usually is. But these, each and every one, are *symbolic superstructures* created above the instinctual level.

If so, we have to understand the system of values as a symbolic universe, with the basic criteria common to all of them. That is, in our terminology, values too are *freely created*; or, in a term more usual in value theory, are *freely posited*. It is understandable that these chosen or posited values are partly taken from the biological repertoire. That is where universal human values come from: individual happiness, survival of the species, the Golden Rule, the Categorical Imperative. They are universal because stemming from "the common structure of man and the common requirements of social existence in the social world" (Muller, 1960, p. 47). But man can also choose differently—and does so in suicide and martyrdom. The martyr is a being who chooses values overriding biological survival and the accepted symbolisms of his society. The Christian martyrs did not die for social improvement or greater happiness of the Roman people; they were convinced that the world and society were doomed and the Day of Judgment was near. They died for their faith, that is, their symbolic construct of God and the world. The same is true—*mutatis mutandis*—for every hero or martyr. In this sense, values are freely created or posited. The range of values understandably goes from *common human* to those that are *idiosyncratic* of a particular culture, society, community or individual. Men have invented the strangest totems and taboos to which they cling sometimes more strongly than to reason or survival. This is so because values are freely created.

This, it seems, gives a tolerably realistic expression of what the existentialists say in their obscure language: that the human condition—in contrast to the animal which is safely guided by its instinctual equipment—is in *free decision*, that is, decision for one of the symbolic structures man creates himself. This is the Dignity of Man—a motive one can easily follow from the beautiful Oration so entitled by the Renaissance mystic, Pico della Mirandola, to Kierkegaard and contemporary existentialists. When creating man, Pico tells, God had pre-empted all treasures, archetypes and niches in the world, having given them, with a rigidly determined nature, to plants, animals and angels. But man was created with the highest of gifts, as a being neither earthly nor heavenly, mortal nor immortal, but endowed with free decision. So he may become a vegetating plant, a rapacious animal, or an angel and son of God.

This is spoken in individualistic terms. But the same line of thought also carries in society and the problems of our time.

Some years ago I was impressed by a booklet by Dr. Chester Barnard, past president of General Electric, the Rockefeller and National Science Foundations, which was a lecture on business morals (1958). In the course of a long executive career, Barnard said, he had observed a strange phenomenon. A business, corporation and the like has to make decisions not only at the technical and legal levels but also of a moral nature. But then, it turns out, the principles of traditional ethics, such as the Ten Commandments or the Golden Rule, offer no guidance. Barnard tells of a conference on a Just and Durable Peace, held in 1944 under the chairmanship of Mr. John Foster Dulles. The theologians, he says, were talking in terms of a nomadic society of sheep, lambs and shepherds. The economists proceeded from artificial assumptions on maximation of profit, neglecting the study of business as such and the entrepreneurial functions. The men of affairs were highly loquacious but singularly inarticulate except in technicalities. So the ineptitude of this conference—and presumably innumerable others—was in the fact that while traditional morals gives precepts for the behavior of the individual, there is no code for the behavior of complex social organizations. In fact, such social entities do have rules of behavior different from individual morals so that "there are certain circumstances where it would be immoral, from the standpoint of responsible representative behavior, not to do things immoral and even illegal from a personal point of view."

Barnard's problem, of course, is by no means new even though couched in modern terms. It is the old problem of Machiavelli's precepts to his *Principe*, of the immoralities and atrocities which Machiavelli recommended but as law-abiding Florentine citizen and decent human being would not have committed himself. It is the problem of the *ius gentium* or international law tossed around since the jurists of the seventeenth century and still unsolved by the United Nations: that the individual in a society is bound by moral and legal rules and can be policed and prosecuted if he breaks them, but that the same is not applicable to social entities.

This is the natural history of twilight figures like Richelieu's Father Joseph, the infamous Grey Eminence of whom Aldous Huxley (1941) drew that extraordinary portrait: a saintly man, without ambition, ascetic, abnegating himself and renouncing any claim to fame or glory; and at the same time serving his Leviathan—called France in this particular instance—with incredible ruthlessness, with the foulest imaginable tricks, cold-bloodedly sacrificing an untold number of victims at his Moloch's altar in the crucible of the Thirty Years' War. With variations (who wouldn't remember Sophocles' *Antigone*), the same theme has been played over and over again in history; leading to such burlesques as the "Catholic King" of France warring "The Most Christian Majesty" of Spain, with respective prayers and Te Deums sung to the same Almighty for successful slaying of the enemy; and to their modern counterparts.

Coming back to Barnard, we can define the problem more clearly. We remember what previously has been said about symbolic structures as basic of human culture, their autonomous development, and their capability of putting man into the unfortunate position of the Sorcerer's Apprentice. In legalistic terms, according to Barnard: Social systems such as corporations and the like are entities which, by means of a legal fiction, gain the attributes of a personality and act, and are morally and legally entitled to act, as if they were real persons or individuals. Something similar applies to governments, nations, states, etc. But then the moral concepts applying to social systems are different from those applying to individuals. So organizations can do and actually do with impunity many things which would be immoral and punishable in the individual, and conflicts naturally arise between the moral values in the individual and in the superordinate social sphere. Incidentally, Marx was perhaps more perspicacious than the champions of Free Enterprise, with their simple-minded cops and robbers, white and black philosophy of good Free World and bad Communist guys; recognizing that the fault is not so much in the moral depravity of "capitalists" as it is in the system, that is, in the structure of superordinate entities.

Here we have at least a partial answer to Nietzsche's Revaluation of Values and his question why traditional values and ideals have proved to be inadequate. The nihilism Nietzsche found in our age would mean not so much that traditional values have broken down as that a value system necessary for our complicated civilization has not yet evolved. The traditional ethical codes give rules for individual behavior, but none for those complicated social systems that have arisen, where the *dramatis personae* are not human beings, but abstract entities acting as if they were individuals, by means of legal or political fiction. Operating the colossal social structures of our time—from businesses to national states to mankind as a whole—with the ethical concepts of a nomadic bronze-age society of three thousand years ago is like operating an atomic reactor with the technology of a bushman. At the same time, it becomes clear why this problem—notwithstanding its long history—has become acute in our period. The reason is simply that never before was the individual so entangled, controlled and governed in his most private affairs by impersonal and hence often inhuman social forces. Moral exhortation to the individual and even his personal honesty are patently ineffective; the problem is to expand moral codes to the inclusion of higher social entities and, at the same time, safeguard the individual from being devoured by the social Leviathan.

## Enter the Professor

I would like to close on a somewhat lighter note, by a tribute to that slightly ridiculous figure, the professor. Our society certainly keeps him in his appointed place in the human pecking order: he definitely ranks below the manager of the five-and-ten at the next street corner, not to speak of the medical practitioner as modern shaman, second-rate television starlets, fashion models or boxers; with the possible exception of the case when he helps in creating the superbomb or invents a particularly efficient advertisement for deodorants. There is not much to boast about.

However, he has a secret vengeance. Ideas do move matter; and in a sense professors are the hidden marionette players of history—those who create world views, values, problems and solutions; in short, that symbolic backdrop against which every scene of the great drama of history is enacted.

The way nobleman and serf felt and experienced themselves in the Middle Ages was invented by the professors of the time—that is, the Fathers of the Church. The Renaissance, which literally created a new man, was the work of professors, even though they were not called so at the time: of Leon Battista Alberti, the Medicean Academy, Leonardo, Michelangelo, and the rest. The Thirty Years' War, which destroyed a third of the population of Central Europe, was a theological argument between St. Augustine and St. Thomas, translated into the power struggle of European princes and into bloody battlefields. The French Revolution and the United States were inventions of Voltaire, Rousseau and the French Encyclopedists. The Soviet Union was drafted by Karl Marx in the circular reading room of the British Museum. And so it goes to the present day. The *Weltanschauung*, the view of life and the world, of the man in the street—the chap who repairs your car or sells you an insurance policy—is a product of Lucretius Carus, Newton, Locke, Darwin, Adam Smith, Ricardo, Freud and Watson—even though you may safely bet that the high school or even university graduate has never heard of most of them or knows of Freud only through the *Dear Abbey* column of his newspaper. It is we who, in the last resort, *manufacture the glasses* through which people look at the world and at themselves—little as they may know it, and little as they are aware of who it was who put the glasses on their metaphorical or metaphysical nose.

I dare say we are the great spectacle makers in history. This is the reason why the intellectual endeavor is more than gathering facts or making clever gadgets. It is a tremendous responsibility; and we have to face it.

PART TWO

# Toward a New "Natural Philosophy"

## The Open System of Science

You, the reader, may wonder about that old-fashioned term "natural philosophy" in the title of this essay. Is it not the hallmark of modern science that it got rid of obsolete philosophy? Have modern positivists—including the Vienna School where I myself started more than forty years ago—worked in vain and am I going to reinvoke the ghosts of metaphysics? Do I wish to revivify medieval superstition in the age of nuclear physics and molecular biology?

A slightly mischievous answer would be that science and philosophy never got rid of metaphysics and that the metaphysics of positivism is a particularly naïve and superficial one, as we had the opportunity to observe with regard to the myth of robot man. However, I have a somewhat deeper motivation. Science, starting with Newton's *magnum opus*, which carried the title of "Natural Philosophy," has two aspects. One, of course, is the explanation and control of happenings, and this is alone what distinguishes science from moot speculation. But there is also the other viewpoint, namely "natural philosophy." Any theory of wider scope implies a world view. If we are speaking of the Copernican revolution, it was not only a question whether the orbits of the planets were calculated somewhat more exactly than was done in Ptolemy's geocentric system (as a matter of fact, this was hardly achieved either in Copernicus' work or in the publicity Galileo gave to the new system of the world). The orbit of Mars and the other planets was hardly a human concern or of general interest to the sixteenth century, except perhaps for astrologers in their shady business. What we mean by the Copernican revolution is the tremendous change in the world outlook, putting man from his safe niche in the center of the universe into the infinities of space. In the same sense, any major development in science changes the world outlook and is "natural philosophy" or "metascience," to use a modern expression.

So far as the word "new" is concerned, new sciences were invented quite a number of times. Typical of human predilection and predicament, the first *Scienza Nuova* was that of artillery, according to the title of a book by Tartaglia in 1537. In 1638 followed Galileo's New Science of Mechanics; in 1725 the New Science of Giambattista Vico, roughly corresponding to what nowadays we would call a theory of history. These are illustrious predecessors, and it is not very original to say that our time is one of a new Scientific Revolution.

However, I shall not talk about particle physics, molecular biology, automation, atomic bombs or astronautics, which come to mind as foremost marvels of modern science. Rather I am going to discuss a reorientation of scientific thought, less well known and publicized but perhaps even more "revolutionary" in the long run. Assuredly, it is still in an early stage, insufficient in its expression, far from the exactness of the conventional "hard" sciences; nevertheless, there are developments in which all sciences —from physics to sociology and history—in some way appear to converge.

The world view of yesterday, the so-called mechanistic universe, was a world of "blind laws of nature" and of physical entities moving at random. Chaos was the oft-quoted blind play of atoms. By accident, organic compounds and eventually self-replicating molecules appeared on the primeval earth as precursors of life. It was no less chaotic happening when, according to current theory of evolution, life proceeded to higher forms by way of random mutations and selection in equally accidental changes of environment. By another unexplainable accident, mind and consciousness somewhere arose as an epiphenomenon of the evolution of the nervous system. In the same sense, human personality, according to behaviorism and psychoanalysis, was a chance product of nature and nurture, some small part being played by the hereditary equipment, and a large part by accidental events in early childhood and subsequent conditioning. Human history, finally, was one damned thing after the other, without rhyme or reason, according to a famous dictum of the historian H. A. L. Fisher, emulating Shakespeare's Cosmic Idiot.

Now, it appears, we are seeking for another basic outlook—*the world as organization.* This claim—if it can be verified—would profoundly change the categories of our thinking and influence our practical attitudes.

Warren Weaver, co-author of information theory, has given this an oft-quoted expression (1948). Classical science, Weaver said, was concerned with *linear or one-way causality*, cause followed by effect, relations between two or a few variables. For example, the relation between one sun and one planet permits the stupendous calculations of celestial mechanics, but already the three-body problem is unsolvable in principle and can be approached only by approximations. As psychologists, we may think of the S-R scheme, with the stimulus as independent and the response as dependent variable. Or else, science was concerned with *unorganized complexity*, that is, statistical phenomena as the outcome of chance events. The prototype is thermodynamics, e.g., the goings-on in a volume of gas. We cannot run after each of the innumerable molecules in the container, but their resulting average behavior is expressed in the second law of thermodynamics and its many derivatives. Similarly, statistical laws apply in genetics, sociology—think of the forecast of the number of suicides or of car collisions over the Labor Day weekend—and many other fields. The insurance business is based on the fact that the number of car accidents, mortality and the like are predictable, even though each individual case is different and results from a multitude of undefined causes.

Now, however, we are confronted with problems of another sort—problems of *organized complexity*. If the principles of classical physics, such as the laws of gravitation and mechanics, were concerned with undirected events and "blind forces of nature," the quest for organizational laws now becomes apparent. Organization runs right through all levels of reality and science. An atom is an organization (as Whitehead already knew), and the perplexities of present-day physics seem to derive from the fact that physicists have discovered a hundred or so elementary particles but are still looking for "laws of organization." Structural chemistry explores the organization of molecules from simple ones to intricate and still partly unexplained, high-molecular structures encountered in the living world. Molecular biology owes its triumphs to organizational concepts such as the Watson-Crick model of DNA, the genetic code, the order of processes in protein synthesis, which widely surpass biochemical notions of a few years ago.

In the life sciences, the same postulate appears under the title of "organismic biology." As I have said for some thirty years, not without encountering strong resistance, the proper study of biology is "the order and organization of parts and processes at all levels of the living world." Strangely, "organismic biology" is now hailed as new and a necessary complement to molecular biology (e.g., Dobzhansky, 1966; Dubos, 1964, 1967; Commoner, 1961) without, on the American side, any mention of the present author, although his role is recognized everywhere else, including the U.S.S.R. and the East European countries (e.g., Ungerer, 1966; Blandino, 1960; Tribiño, 1946; Kanaev, 1966; Kamarýt, 1963; Bendmann, 1963; Afanasjew, 1962), and nothing new has been added to his statements.[9]

In sociology, Sorokin (e.g., 1966) has given the problem a lucid expression, distinguishing "the microcosm of lawlessness" in undetermined microphysical events (and nonrecurrent socio-cultural phenomena), statistical regularities in "congeries" of macrophysics and psychosocial mass phenomena, and organizational laws, exemplified by the organization of genes, but presumably also discoverable in socio-cultural systems. "Systems," it may be safely said, is the most discussed notion in present sociology.

The same is true of technology and allied fields. The complexities of modern technology and commerce have led to new fields and jobs going under the names of systems research, systems analysis, systems engineering, operations research, human engineering and others (cf., for example, Ackoff 1959; Hall, 1962; Boguslaw, 1965; de Hanika, 1965). These developments use concepts of general system theory (in the narrower sense), of cybernetics, information theory, game and decision theories, linear programming, queueing theory and others, and are connected with electronics, computer science, armament research, etc.

Instead of militaristic or utopian examples, I like to quote a homely one: We cross the continent or ocean by jet in a few hours, in order to spend at least an equal number of hours in nerve-racking waiting at airports and being led around (though by a sometimes pretty stewardess) like a herd of cattle. With 120-miles-per-hour cars and multimillion-dollar freeways it takes longer—and is much more dangerous—to go from one end of Los Angeles or New York to the other than in the days of horse-and-buggy. Many similar situations show the contrast between a fabulous physical technology and a deplorable lack in techniques of organization.

Thus the intricacies of modern life and technology have elicited a novel development, in industry, commerce and military enterprise, of "systems research." Let us hear an exponent of operations research:

> In the last two decades we have witnessed the emergence of the "system" as a key concept in scientific research. Systems, of course, have been studied for centuries, but something new has been added. . . . The tendency to study systems as an entity rather than as a conglomeration of parts is consistent with the tendency in contemporary science

> no longer to isolate phenomena in narrowly confined contexts, but rather to open interactions for examination and to examine larger and larger slices of nature. Under the banner of *systems research* (and its many synonyms) we have also witnessed a convergence of many more specialized contemporary scientific developments. . . . These research pursuits and many others are being interwoven into a cooperative research effort involving an ever-widening spectrum of scientific and engineering disciplines. We are participating in what is probably the most comprehensive effort to attain a synthesis of scientific knowledge yet made (Ackoff, 1959).

Last but not least, the same trend penetrates into politics and management of national affairs. Political leaders ask for the "systems approach" to problems such as pollution, traffic congestion, crime control, health and urban blight, this being labeled as a "revolutionary new concept" and possibly "the only real solution to problems which are among the nation's most important and vexing" (Carter, 1966).

Enough has been said to make clear that we have to do with a powerful force in contemporary thought and life. Of course, this is not to say that it is a brand-new invention. The historian of science always finds that the number of germinal ideas is limited and that they tend to reappear, spiral-wise, at increasingly higher levels of sophistication. For example, the three basic conceptions in biology, mechanistic, vitalistic and organismic, ultimately go back as far as to Democritus, Aristotle and Hippocrates, respectively; the organismic idea can be traced to Claude Bernard, Goethe, Paracelsus, and further. In sociology, Sorokin (1964) has given a detailed historical survey up to modern times. But if we must avoid falling into the trap of "new Columbianism" (Sorokin, 1956)—congratulating ourselves on having discovered new continents which, in fact, were already trodden in the past—there is a difference between the Normans touching Vineland and the exploration of the continent. Similarly, it will be fair to say that science only now has entered a stage permitting serious exploration of the new realm.

Broadly speaking, the modern "systems" movement has three roots. One was the demand for a "general theory of systems," posed by myself shortly after the Second War; the second, cybernetics finding a powerful expression in Wiener's book (1948); the third, the demands of engineering in complex production processes, man-machine systems, armament research and the like.

We can summarize the motivations for what we may briefly call an organismic or system approach, in three statements.

First—until recently, physics was the only "exact" science, that is, a consistent conceptual structure allowing for explanation, prediction and control of nature. More recently, the biological, behavioral and social sciences have come into their own and appear to demand new forms of conceptualization, models, laws. Thus a *generalization of scientific concepts* appears to be necessary.

Second—in biology, the behavioral and social sciences we encounter many phenomena which are not found in inanimate nature and for which no concepts were provided in the system of physics. We cannot speak of living things and of behavior except in a functional manner, that is, regarding their parts and processes as organized in view of the maintenance, development, evolution, etc., of the system. This is not an anthromorphic projection of the purposiveness of our own actions, a vitalistic or metaphysical prejudice; it is a simple fact of observation, a question which is asked—and empirically answered—vis-à-vis any organ, structure, process, enzyme, hormone, or whatever the object of biological research. On the contrary, to disregard or bypass this all-pervasive order is metaphysical prejudice.

Organismic processes as a rule are so ordered as to maintain the system. But this makes no sense within the conventional categories of physics. From this viewpoint, there is no difference between physical and chemical processes taking place in a living organism and those in a corpse; both follow the same laws of physics and chemistry—and that's all that can be said. To the biologist and physician, however, there is a profound difference between events so ordered as to maintain the system, and those running wild to destroy it. What are the principles of order and organization? What does "health" or "norm" mean in contrast to "disease" and "pathology"? Nothing, so far as laws of physics and chemistry are concerned and mechanistic philosophy is adopted. But without these and similar notions there would be no science of medicine and indeed of biology. Moreover, conventional physics appears to be directly contravened or violated by what is going on in the living world. Physical processes follow the second law of thermodynamics, which prescribes that they proceed toward increasing entropy, that is, more probable states which are states of equilibrium, of uniform distribution and disappearance of existing differentiations and order. But living systems apparently do exactly the opposite. In spite of irreversible processes continually going on, they tend to maintain an organized state of fantastic improbability; they are maintained in states of non-equilibrium; they even develop toward increasingly improbable states, increasing differentiation and order, as is manifest both in the individual development of an organism and in evolution from the famous amoeba to man.

Similar considerations apply in the psychosocial sciences. Furthermore, in the biological, behavioral and socio-cultural fields events directed toward future goals appear to be prevalent. Physical causality provides no model for this; more precisely, goal-directedness and dependence on future events are declared to be unscientific phantoms or metaphysics. The essential point is not that physico-chemical explanations are still lacking for many life phenomena (as is unfortunately the case, but is increasingly remedied by the progress of research); but that the traditional categories of mechanistic science do not suffice (or rather exclude) basic empirical aspects. It appears, therefore, that an *expansion of categories,* models and theory is needed adequately to deal with the biological, behavioral and social universes.

Third—as we shall see presently, there are conceptions emerging which appear to meet these demands. In contrast to the progressive specialization in modern science, this new sort of models is *interdisciplinary*; the same abstract model applies to different content, in different fields or disciplines. In other terms, phenomena different in content often show *isomorphism* in their formal structure.

What we have said in the way of postulates is exactly what is taking place. New scientific disciplines have emerged which are *expansions of the system of traditional physics*; they are especially concerned with *concepts and models arising from the biological and behavioral sciences*; and they are essentially *interdisciplinary*, applicable to different fields.

These developments are hardly older than some twenty or thirty years; no wonder they are far from the maturity of the "hard" sciences. It appears wiser to contemplate that it took some three hundred years—from the so-called terminists of the University of Paris in the thirteenth century to Galileo and Newton—to arrive at the elementary laws of mechanics which now are in the reach of schoolboys; or that it needs a high-caliber historian of science to extract Kepler's famous laws from the mixture of careful observations, creative intuition, and neo-Pythagorean fantasies in his work. We have to be patient if a new trend has not yet reached the maturity of physics considered paradigmatic by positivist philosophers.

In summary: There are recent developments, loosely circumscribed by the concept of system, which try to answer the demands mentioned. In contrast to the progressive and necessary specialization of modern science, they let us hope for a new integration and conceptual organization. Speaking in terms of natural philosophy, as against the world as chaos, a new conception of the world as organization seems to emerge.

This development is indicated by the appearance of a bundle of new disciplines: *general system theory*, *cybernetics*, *information*, *decision* and *game theories*, and others. They differ in basic assumptions, models, mathematical techniques and intentions and occasionally contradict each other. They agree, however, in being "systems sciences," concerned with aspects hitherto neglected and, in one way or the other, with problems of interaction of many variables, of organization, regulation, goal directedness and the like.

In recent developments of "systems science," two basic trends can be distinguished. For short, they may be termed the "mechanistic" and "organismic" trends.

The *mechanistic trend* is connected with technological, industrial and social developments, such as control techniques, automation, computerization and their application for industrial, military, governmental, etc., purposes. The underlying theory is essentially that of cybernetics, automata, computers and similar "hardware." The enormous strides these developments have made are generally known and widely publicized, and so are their dangers. Improved control techniques, automation and the Cybernetic Society present novel problems to the individual and society, menacing unemployment, use of leisure time in automated society, the robotization of the human individual, new value problems in an economy of abundance instead of an economy of want, overproduction disposable only in the Orwellian way of war, and others.

The *organismic trend* essentially starts from the trite consideration that "an organism is an organized thing"; and we must look for principles and laws concerning "organization," "wholeness," "order of parts and processes," "multivariable interaction" and so forth, to be elaborated by a "general system theory."

Aim and term of general system theory were first introduced by the present author after the Second World War (prior to Wiener's *Cybernetics* of 1948). It soon turned out that a considerable number of scientists in different fields had followed similar lines of thought. This resulted in the formation of the Society for General Systems Research, an affiliate of AAAS which has published *Yearbooks* since 1956.

I am not aware that the late Heinz Werner has used the concept of general system theory. Nevertheless, I believe that this corresponds with his intentions, and is able to provide a theoretical framework for organismic-developmental psychology. For what was Werner's basic idea? To arrive at psychological principles by way of comparison of children, adults, primitives, psychopathological cases, microgeny of mental events, etc., with a sparkling of biological parallels. Generalize this somewhat more, as Arthur Koestler did in his *Act of Creation*, and you will see that similar problems and principles of organization, of progressive differentiation and the like appear in psychology, embryology, formation of the nervous system, cognition, sociological phenomena and many others. The quest of general system theory is to develop a conceptual structure applicable in various phases.

The relation between these two trends deserves some clarification.

## Cybernetics and Its Limitations

The foremost modern systems science in the "mechanistic trend" is cybernetics, in its incarnation in technological marvels of servomechanisms and automation, in the application of cybernetic concepts to biological regulations, and in the social consequences of the Second Industrial Revolution. The interest in these developments is well understandable and deserved in view of the role cybernetic systems, computers and "servos" of many kinds are playing in industry and modern life. Not infrequently, this has led to equating "cybernetics" with "systems theory." This, however, is a misunderstanding that needs correction.

The basic concepts of cybernetics are those of "feedback" and of "information." The minimum elements of a cybernetic system are a "receptor" accepting "stimuli" from outside as input; from this a message is led to a "center," which in some way reacts to the message and, as a rule, amplifies the signals received; the center, in its turn, transmits the message to an "effector," which eventually reacts to the stimulus with a "response" as output. The output, however, is monitored back, by a "feedback" loop, to the receptor, which senses the preliminary response and steers the subsequent action of the system so that eventually the desired result, a "target value" (*Sollwert*), is obtained. In this way, the system is self-regulating.

The function of the cybernetic system further depends on "messages" received from outside and plying between receptor, center and effector, that is, on transmission of a something which, as a rule, is represented by minute quantities of energy but has a "meaning" to the system. This "information" turns out to be a novel physical quantity in comparison to conventional physical measures such as energy and mass. It is measurable in bits, i.e., units of binary decision; and the equation defining information has the structure of negative entropy.

This, in short, is the cybernetic model. It is realized in that simplest example, the familiar thermostat (with a thermometer as "receptor," the output—temperature obtained—of the heating system fed back to the receptor and so controlling the further input of fuel); as well as in machines steering toward a goal (e.g., self-directing missiles) where the deviation from the target is received as message and, by continuous feedback, is progressively minimized so that eventually the missile hits the target. Cybernetic systems usually are of great complexity; but they can always be resolved into feedback circuits; the basic principle remains the same, even when fantastically elaborate arrangements of feedback circuits are superimposed.

As is well known, the cybernetic model was found applicable to a wide range of biological regulations, subsumed under the term of *homeostasis,* i.e., maintenance of important physiological parameters at a constant level. One of the simpler examples is homeothermy, the maintenance of body temperature in warm-blooded animals. Structurally, e.g., represented in a block diagram, homeothermy closely corresponds to the function of a thermostat. Maintenance of the sugar, ion, hormone levels in the blood are a few among many other examples. Similarly, the maintenance of posture, goal-directed movements, and many other phenomena are describable in terms of feedback circuits.[10]

This impressively illustrates the interdisciplinary nature of the cybernetic model, which, while originating in engineering and modern technology, covers a much wider field. The very same model, represented by a block or flow diagram, may be descriptive of, say, regulation in a hydrostatic machine, an electronic device, posture or movement in an animal; that is, the same formal structure applies to systems that are totally different with regard to their material components, the forces applied, the functions performed, and so forth.

At the same time, it is apparent that the identification of cybernetics with systems theory is incorrect. The feedback model is only one, and a rather special, type of self-regulating system. The fact that feedback systems are of wide occurrence in the biological (and psychosocial) realm should not obscure their limitations.

Obviously, the cybernetic model is still "mechanistic" in the sense that it presupposes a "mechanism," that is structural arrangements as indicated above. In behavioral parlance, the cybernetic model is the familiar S-R (or S-O-R) scheme, with the feedback loop added to make the system self-regulating. In contrast, general systems (in the sense of general system theory, see pp. 69 ff.) are non-mechanistic in the sense that regulative behavior is not determined by structural or "machine" conditions but by the interplay of forces.

Speaking in epistemological terms: while the prototype of undirected physical processes is *linear causality* (cause A being followed by effect B), the cybernetic model introduces *circular causality* by way of the feedback loop, and this makes for the self-regulation, goal-directedness, homeostasis, etc., of the system. In contrast, the more general system model is that of *dynamic interaction* between many variables.

Dynamic regulation precedes structural feedback. Consequently, "cybernetic" models particularly apply to "secondary" regulations, but "kinetic" models are required for "primary" regulations. Thus (speaking broadly), regulation of metabolism in the cell (e.g., in respiration or photosynthesis) is based upon a network of reactions in an open system; with progressive evolution, ever more elaborate homeostatic mechanisms, such as nervous and hormonal feedbacks, arise.

Cybernetic systems are "closed" with respect to exchange of matter with environment, and open only to information. For this reason, the cybernetic model does not provide for an essential characteristic of living systems, whose components are continually destroyed in catabolic and replaced in anabolic processes, with corollaries such as growth, development and differentiation.

For the same reason, a cybernetic system cannot be "self-organizing," that is, evolving from a less to a more differentiated state. To be sure, cybernetic systems provided with memory devices can learn, that is, change and increase their organization owing to information input. They cannot undergo processes of differentiation which require input of energy (and matter). In other terms, cybernetic systems can only increase in their entropy content and decrease in information content, information being partly converted into noise but not vice versa (Shannon's Tenth Theorem). Anti-entropic processes presuppose the system's being "open," that is, transfer of matter and energy taking place.

For these reasons, the cybernetic model is of great value because of its interdisciplinary nature, the insight it provides for regulatory, goal-seeking and teleological behavior and the elucidation of many specific phenomena it affords, even when the systems in question are unknown or unidentified in their material structure and contributing processes. It falls short of being a general theory of systems, or providing a new "natural philosophy." While cybernetic research, justly, is ever more intensified and expanded, it appears that the intrinsic limitations of its basic model are being recognized:

> For a time after World War II it seemed that cybernetics might become another such formative branch of science, which would bring together many different fields and impress on them the unity of a new conception that was both profound and understandable.
>
> The recent death of Norbert Wiener provides an occasion

> to observe that the heroic dream is over. Cybernetics remains in the best sense a fundamental idea as well as a popular one, but it has turned out to be less embracing and, in an odd way, less interesting than we had hoped 20 years ago when it was conceived (Bronowski, 1964).

In summary: Feedback systems are a somewhat special case of general systems, characterized by the presence of constraints which lead the process in the way of circular causality and so make it self-regulating. The concept of "general system" is, in comparison, a broader one, and a general theory of systems should embrace dynamic interaction between many variables, maintenance in change of component elements, growth, progressive differentiation, mechanization and centralization, increase in the level of organization and the like.

## General Systems

*General system theory* (in the narrower sense of the term) is a discipline concerned with the general properties and laws of "systems." A system is defined as a complex of components in interaction, or by some similar proposition. System theory tries to develop those principles that apply to systems in general, irrespective of the nature of systems, of their components, and of the relations or "forces" between them. The system components need not even be material, as, for example, in the system analysis of a commercial enterprise where components such as buildings, machines, personnel, money and "good will" of customers enter.

Among systems features are multivariable interaction, maintenance of wholes in the counteraction of component parts, multilevel organization into systems of ever higher order, differentiation, centralization, progressive mechanization, steering and trigger causality, regulation, evolution toward higher organization, teleology and goal-directedness in various forms and ways, etc. The fact that such features—omnipresent in the biological, behavioral and social fields, object of empirical observation both in everyday life and scientific research—are not covered by traditional physicalistic concepts has often led to their being considered as of a metaphysical nature or vitalistic provenience, or even to deny their existence and anathematize their investigation—in contradiction to common sense and to actual practice in the biosocial realms. This epistemological bias, rooted in a mechanistic metaphysics deeply ingrained in the history of Western science, appears to be the main reason for our ignorance with respect to essential problems of life, mind and society when compared with the progress of physics, in which the Newtonian simplification of one-way causality and two-variable problems is highly successful.

Even in physics, however, there are limitations of the latter, such as the classical three-body problem in mechanics and its counterparts in atomic physics. The nonphysicist has no say in these matters; it will, however, hardly encounter objections to say that further development of nuclear physics "requires much experimental work, as well as the development of additional powerful methods for the handling of systems with many, but not infinitely many, particles" (de-Shalit, 1966). Conceptions like the "eightfold path" may be indicative of developments in physics in the line of systems thinking.

In the life sciences progress certainly was tremendous so far as conventional categories proved applicable. However, basic and central problems circumscribed by notions like those mentioned above still are elusive although they are stubborn facts and not anthropomorphic superstition. Hence the necessity of broadening the categories of scientific thought to which we have alluded.

General system theory may be considered a science of "wholeness" or holistic entities which hitherto, that is, under the mechanistic bias, were excluded as unscientific, vitalistic or metaphysical. Within the framework of general system theory these aspects become scientifically accessible. General system, therefore, is an interdisciplinary model which needs, but also is capable of, scientific elaboration and consequently can be applied to concrete phenomena. This is its "scientific" aspect. Like every more general theory or model, it also has its aspects as "metascience" (Jones, in press) or "natural philosophy"; that is, it influences our world outlook; and appears to be broader and more realistic than previous, mechanistic philosophy.

The program is clearly posed; its elaboration has only begun, requires a conceptual reorientation, and is beset with difficulties. As general system theory has to develop concepts, models and laws covering long-neglected aspects of reality, this implies (1) mathematical developments to formulate the concept of "system" and to derive from it features characteristic of systems in general or defined subclasses; (2) application of system considerations to empirical entities and discovery of their laws; whereby (3) phenomena as yet beyond scientific understanding may be opened up to scientific investigation.

Systems and systems principles can be approached by various mathematical techniques, such as classical calculus, group, set, digraph theories, topology, etc. (cf. Rapoport, 1966). Multivariable problems provide a large field for computerization and simulation by electronic devices. No comprehensive theory of systems exists today. Indeed problems encountered (e.g., nonlinear systems; "immense" numbers appearing in system interactions, i.e., orders of magnitude far above, say, the number of particles in the universe but appearing even in systems with a moderate number of interacting components; cf. Ashby, 1964; Hart, 1959; Rapoport, 1959; Repge, 1962), transcend presently available mathematics and presumably require novel approaches. Nevertheless, many system problems can be successfully investigated by way of suitable models, abstractions and simplifications; often elementary mathematics gives surprising results.

If at present general system theory is capable of dealing, in exact terms, with only a limited range of phenomena, while many others can be dealt with only in more or less loose verbal language or not at all, it is well to remember the history of science. Galileo's and Newton's universes were but a minute fraction of the physical world known to nineteenth-century physics, which in turn has increased immeasurably during our lifetime. Perhaps more precisely: System theory probably is in a phase comparable to electrodynamics at the time of Faraday and before Maxwell; principles are intuitively seen, but a genius is needed to provide mathematical theory.

General characteristics as previously indicated recur in different fields and at different levels, such as the living organism, behavioral activities, and sociocultural phenomena. Such entities therefore appear *isomorphic* with respect to certain system characteristics. From this results the fact, surprising at the first look, that for example a generalized kinetics and formally identical laws apply to entities which are intrinsically so different as chemical systems, animal and human populations, and economic processes. On the other hand, this emphasizes the value of general system theory for economy of thinking because principles once established in one field may be transferred to another, still insufficiently known.

Naturally, this must be done with necessary caution, well distinguishing "logical homology" (von Bertalanffy, 1960a) or "nomic isomorphy" (Hempel, 1965)—i.e., structural correspondence in the systems under consideration—from superficial "analogy," which may be totally misleading. This, however, is not a problem peculiar to general systems, but of the discretion generally required in choosing suitable conceptual models for observed phenomena.

The application of system-theoretical considerations has been widespread. It includes—to quote a few widely different examples—application of system principles in engineering; biophysics, particularly in the theory of open systems; biosociology, including economically important systems such as fisheries industry and human societies; relative growth as a measure of differentiation in the organism, in evolution, and in social groups; general principles of growth-in-time; competition between entities at various levels, such as those of molecules, individual organisms, species or economic entities; the mathematical description and prediction of social trends such as the armament race in the modern world. In such cases, the isomorphy of laws (e.g., allometric growth in the organism and social groups, kinetic principles applying in physical chemistry and in population dynamics) becomes apparent.[11]

The present consideration can neither review the status of the formal theory of systems, nor reproduce substantive investigations in any detail. Rather, we intend to discuss a few problems of broader implications, of "natural philosophy."

## Open Systems: The Living Flame

It is a basic characteristic of living systems that they are maintained in a continuous exchange of components. This is manifest at all levels: exchange of chemical components in the cell, of cells in the multicellular organism, of individuals in the population, etc. "Organic structures are themselves expression of an ordered process, and they are only maintained in and by this process. Therefore, the primary order of organic processes must be sought in the processes themselves, not in pre-established structures" (von Bertalanffy, 1960a, p. 17).

This leads to an important classification, that of *closed* and *open systems*. Organisms are open systems. To be sure, they are not the only open systems in existence: a flame is a simple example of a physical system that is "open" (hence the old simile between fire and life); and chemical technology ever more uses open reaction systems in contrast to conventional closed-system or batch processes.

Nevertheless, the distinction of closed and open systems is a very basic one, and it leads to problems such as contrasts between the physical and living worlds, problems of time, of evolution, of self-organization and differentiation, of probable and negentropic trends, of laws new compared to those of traditional physics.

Nothwithstanding or because of the fact that a large part of my own labor has been devoted to the study of open systems and their application to biological phenomena, I shall limit the present considerations to some brief remarks. The insight that a living system maintains itself in the change of components is, of course, as old as Heraclitus' *panta rhei,* and an expression of the basic fact of metabolism. Nevertheless—a phenomenon not unknown in the history of science—it was only in recent years that the conception was developed in a scientific way.

In fact, the theory of open systems is not older than some twenty or thirty years. Physical chemistry used to be limited to the investigation of closed systems which, for obvious reasons, are easier to investigate but represent a special case; for one can always arrive from the theory of open to that of closed systems by equating transport terms to zero, but not vice versa. Since then, kinetics of open systems was elaborated which shows remarkable features. Similarly, an expansion of thermodynamics known as *irreversible thermodynamics* took place: while "classical" thermodynamics or thermostatics is concerned with closed systems, reversible processes and equilibria, now open systems, irreversible processes and nonequilibrium states were incorporated.

Again, the open-system model has a wide range of application in biological, physiological, social and other problems (cf. von Bertalanffy, 1953, 1964b). One interesting facet is that expansion of theory led to the incorporation of phenomena which previously—that is, in physics of closed systems—appeared to contradict or violate physics, and therefore were considered vitalistic attributes to be explained only by a goal-seeking agency or "ghost in the machine." Two examples—one kinetic, one thermodynamic—may make this clear.

It was a supposedly vitalistic feature of the organism that in many respects it behaves *equifinally;* that is, the same final state or "goal" may be reached from different initial conditions or in different ways. This, as a rule, does not happen in nonliving systems; here the state at a time $t$ is unequivocally defined by the state at a previous time, $t_0$. Not so in many biological regulations. A famous example comes from experimental embryology: a normal ovum, e.g., of the sea urchin, a part of an ovum, a half, a quarter or even an eighth of it, two ova fused, etc., may yield the same result, a normal sea urchin larva. As a matter of fact, this equifinality was considered to be the main "proof" of vitalism by the German biologist and philosopher Hans Driesch: if a developing ovum is a "machine," obviously this cannot yield the same product—a normal organism—if it is divided, two "machines" are fused, or the developing ovum is disturbed in other ways. Similarly, a growing organism may arrive at the same final state—a certain species-specific adult size—from different initial sizes at birth, or after disturbances or temporary inhibition of the growth process. It turns out, however, that equifinality is not vitalistic and is (in principle, though often not in detail) an attribute of open systems. If and when an open system develops toward a time-independent state, a so-called "steady state," this is independent of the initial conditions and defined only by the parameters, such as reaction and transport rates, of the system.

Another aspect is even more exciting, being answered in certain respects but posing formidable problems in others. For well over a hundred years, a basic antithesis was noticed between inanimate and animate nature. The direction of physical events is prescribed by the second principle of thermodynamics, which says that the general trend of physical happenings is toward most probable states, that is, maximum entropy and progressive destruction of differentiation and order. Take, as simplest example, a gas within a chamber, with "hot" molecules (i.e., molecules having a high velocity) concentrated in one half, "cold" molecules in the other. The system will tend toward thermal equilibrium, that is, a state of most probable distribution of the molecules, which means disappearance of the temperature gradient and uniform distribution, defined by maximum entropy. The same applies generally. "Higher," directed forms of energy (e.g., mechanical, electric, chemical) are dissipated, that is, progressively converted into the lowest form of energy, i.e., undirected heat movement of molecules; chemical systems tend toward equilibria with maximum entropy; machines wear out owing to friction; in communication channels, information can only be lost by conversion of messages into noise but not vice versa, and so forth.

Living systems present a different picture. They are maintained in a state of fantastic improbability, in spite of innumerable irreversible processes continually going on. Even more, organisms —in individual ontogeny as well as in phylogenetic evolution— develop toward more improbable states, toward increase of differentiation and higher order of matter.

Here, again, we seem to have a fundamental contrast between nonliving and living nature, which frequently served as vitalistic argument.

Thermodynamics of open systems gives an answer which, in principle, is simple. In open systems, we have not only *entropy production* owing to irreversible processes taking place in the system; we also have *entropy transport,* by way of introduction of material which may carry high free energy or "negative entropy." Hence, the entropy balance in an open system may well be negative, that is, the system may develop toward states of higher improbability, order and differentiation (although, of course, entropy increases in the larger system consisting of the organism and its environment). This is what actually applies in living organisms.

It should be mentioned, though, that this is the beginning rather than the end of inquiry. As has just been said, development toward states of higher differentiation and order is *thermodynamically permitted* in open systems. But what is the thermodynamic definition of steady states eventually attained in this development? Equilibria in closed systems are defined as states of maximum entropy. A thermodynamic definition of steady states in open systems is still lacking. Prigogine, to whom irreversible thermodynamics is indebted for important developments, has proposed an answer known as Prigogine's Theorem: Steady states in open systems are defined by minimum entropy production (the latter, like entropy, a mathematically defined function). Unfortunately, Prigogine's Theorem is valid only under rather severe restrictions which do not seem to apply to developing systems in biology. The theorem holds good for certain transport processes (such as the so-called Knudsen effect) but not for the biologically most important case of steady states in chemical reaction systems. Recently, the Russian physicist Trincher (1965) made a bold proposal, adding to the entropy principle in physics "principles of adaptation" and "evolution" in biology which, mathematically similar to the first, define trends toward entropy decrease and increasing information content. Unfortunately, this answer is hardly satisfactory. For the entropy principle in physics is not only a mathematical description of a general trend of events, it has its explanation in statistical mechanics: according to Boltzmann's derivation, increasing entropy represents the trend toward most probable distributions. Trincher's biological principles, in contrast, have no physical basis presently known—quite apart from the fact that—surprisingly in a Russian investigator—a sort of dualism between physical and living nature appears to be reintroduced by Trincher's proposal.

Here we are at the very limits of present science and "natural philosophy." We do not possess an answer, but some further considerations may help in understanding the problem.

First, it should be remembered that formation of structures, local increase of order and decrease of entropy, do not contradict the second principle. Consider the formation of a crystal from a supersaturated solution (cf. Haase, 1957). In terms of probability, a congregation of particles in a small volume and complex pattern would be a most improbable event indeed. But crystal formation is an ordinary happening, and it well obeys the second principle. The reason is that the random heat movement of molecules is superseded by the lattice forces exerted by the particles; and the second principle is obeyed because the local order achieved is "paid for" by an entropy increase in the wider system, crystal plus solution, appearing as heat of crystallization.

This example can well be generalized in a biologically relevant fashion. Biological structures, too, are possible because of the existence of "organizational" forces and laws. These are well known in the chemical realm as valencies, van der Waals forces and the like. They are partly known and progressively investigated in high-molecular chemistry; and we seem to "see" them, without at present being able to pronounce their law, in the wide realm of electron-microscopic structures between biochemical entities and microscopic cell structures. Remember, for example, the structures of viruses; the hierarchy of fibrillar arrangements from threadlike molecules to microscopic fibers to the macroscopic muscle; the common organization of cilia and flagella with eleven bundles of fibrils, nine peripheral and a pair in the center. No doubt, progress in high-molecular chemistry, electron microscopy, molecular biology and allied fields will progressively elucidate "laws of organization" at the various biological levels.

Nevertheless, stable structures such as crystals, fibrils and the like are one thing, and structures maintained or elaborated in a flow of matter are another. Looking broadly at biological phenomena, one can hardly deny that two very general phenomenological principles obtain: one of the maintenance of living systems in continuous flow of ordered process, and another of a trend toward increasing differentiation and order ("anamorphosis" in a term of the German biologist Woltereck). I noted this in 1929; and Needham already in 1934, at the close of his monumental work on Chemical Embryology, noted the connection with an expansion of thermodynamics, not yet existent at the time.

The first feature of "maintenance of system in an ordered flow of processes" is, in principle though not in detail, accountable for by the theory of steady states in open systems. In well-investigated cases, such as photosynthesis and cell respiration, the network of reactions is well known and described in mathematical terms; and numerous phenomena in growth, excitation, population dynamics, etc., are elucidated by essentially the same model. It is the second problem which presents particular difficulties because of aspects alien to familiar physics.

Higher "organization" and hierarchically higher levels are often achieved by unison of elements to systems according to "organizational" laws. Such is the case in the well-known scale of nature from elementary particles to atoms, molecules, molecular arrangements, submicroscopic structures, cells, multicellular organisms and so on. However, there is something more.

We may remember that Heinz Werner, in psychology, proclaimed as basic principle the progressive differentiation from primitive, amorphous or, to use his term, "syncretic" states to increasing organization; which was, of course, a major distinction of the developmental approach versus current robot and learning theories. Speaking generally, in comparison to hierarchies by assembly of formerly separate parts, "differentiation hierarchies" are characteristic of the living world. The zygote and cell assembly it yields are differentiated into germ layers, tissues, and organs of the multicellular body. Evolution "from amoeba to man" differentiates the basic life functions, first present in a single cell, into a multitude of tissues, organs, specialized functions, behavioral mechanisms and so forth. Social organizations pass from a primitive amorphous state to the formation of ever more elaborate groups, organizations, division of labor, etc. Something similar may even apply in cosmology when, according to one theory, the primeval atom, with the great bang at the beginning of the world process, burst out to differentiate into a hundred or so species of atoms of the chemical elements.

Differentiation of a material system, as previously noted, is not possible in machines receiving only information as input because it requires energy for being performed. It is energetically possible in open systems, about the simplest example being the Knudsen experiment mentioned: An ideal gas is kept in two connected chambers held under different temperatures, pressure being equal at the beginning; with energy input in the way of keeping the chambers at different temperatures, a simplest differentiation or order is obtained in a steady state eventually attained where, in continuous exchange of molecules, pressure (density of molecules) remains constant (and different) in the two compartments.

Obviously this model of "heteronomous" differentiation owing to conditions imposed from outside (different temperature in the compartments) is insufficient with respect to "autonomous" or self-differentiation such as that in a developing embryo, which is not directed by outside factors.

In organisms another agent enters, i.e., the genetic code of the zygote which directs the developmental process, presumably by enzymes issued according to the specifications transmitted in the DNA chains of the chromosomes. (The sequence of nucleotide triplets in DNA transmits "information" in complex but largely elucidated processes: messenger RNA is formed according to the DNA template; this directs synthesis of species-specific proteins under cooperation of ribosomes, transfer RNA, enzymes, and the energy-yielding ATP system; the proteins so formed act as enzymes directing developmental processes.) It would appear that the minimum requirements of a "living organism" exhibiting self-differentiation are an open (metabolizing) system providing the energy required, and a genetic code steering the process by way of stored information.

With respect to genetic information, the problem is pushed back a further step. If we do not wish to accept a gratuitous and rather fantastic preformation, supposing that all information or codons directing human development were already present in the primeval amoeba, we must grant that the amount of genetic information has increased in evolution. But this is another dimension in the negentropic trend of the living world.

Such and possibly other aspects will have to be integrated in order to arrive at a theory of a very profound problem in the living world. We are not willing to make a new "vital force" or "entelechy" out of presently unsolved questions; but we have to look forward to a new breakthrough, possibly in the way of further generalizations and unification of thermodynamics, information theory and molecular genetics.

## A Glance at Evolution

This necessarily leads to the problem of evolution. Current evolutionary theory (if it does not ignore the problems under discussion) presumes that they are explained by random events. This, by a sort of short cut, would eliminate the troublesome questions of the origin of the genetic code and its evolution, of "anamorphosis" in the living world, its negentropic trend, etc. Whether this short cut is possible is therefore of paramount importance for our natural philosophy and lastly our image of man.

As will be known, modern "synthetic theory" of evolution is essentially Darwin's doctrine, incorporating, however, genetics, cytology, molecular biology, ecology, population dynamics and other fields in a monumental compass. Evolution is based upon accidental hereditary variations, which in the majority are harmful or indifferent. In rare cases, however, they are advantageous and therefore favored by selection. Accumulating over long periods, mutations at random directed by selection lead to progressive adaptation and evolution. This is Darwin's doctrine. Synthetic theory has clarified and deepened the Darwinian concepts. Mutation now is defined as a change in the genetic code of DNA in the chromosomes; selection is differential reproduction, that is, those mutants will eventually prevail which produce the largest number of offspring under given environmental circumstances.

What has not changed is the gist of Darwinian explanation. Mutations are at random; to use a well-known simile (Beadle, 1963), they are comparable to copying errors of a not very careful typist, which sometime happen when the DNA code of the chromosomes is duplicated; or in another famous metaphor, evolution is "monkey business," comparable to the labor of that interesting animal as he shuffles a heap of letters through the eons and, after an indefinite number of meaningless combinations, eventually comes out with a copy of *Hamlet*. Evolution is given its direction by selection, that is, differential reproduction under prevailing environmental conditions. Evolution therefore is "outer-directed."

Similar considerations apply to the problem of origin of life, which is widely discussed at present. As this implies even more extrapolation and speculative elements, we shall bypass it with a brief note.

One difficulty is in the circularity of the argument. It is said that spontaneously arising, primeval "living matter" (e.g., proteins acting as enzymes, reduplicating nucleoproteins) was united, by "selection" of more successful "mutants," into systems, first simple protobionta, subsequently precursors of cells, cells, etc. But, so far as we know, such molecules are formed only by interplay in a system, either the natural cell or suitable arrangements instituted by the experimenter: enzymes are formed only in the presence of nucleoproteins, which direct the arrangement of amino acids in their protein chain; for formation of nucleoproteins enzymes (plus energy-yielding systems such as ATP) are required. And even if complex molecules like nucleoproteins and enzymes are considered as being "given," there is no known principle of physics and chemistry which, in reactions at random, would favor their "survival" against their decay; rather this is contrary to the second principle of thermodynamics according to which a "soup" containing proteins, nucleoproteins, enzymes, etc., would tend to chemical equilibrium, that is, breakdown of "improbable" proteins, etc., into "probable" simple compounds (as happens after the death of any living system). Selection, i.e., favored survival of "better" precursors of life, already presupposes self-maintaining, complex, open systems which may compete; therefore selection cannot account for the origin of such systems. It is a new version of the old question which is first, hen or egg. Here the question appears to rest at present until some essentially new principle is discovered. (A philosophically astute discussion, although not reviewing the many pertinent data, can be found in Harris, 1965.)

We have, of course, to accept and take for granted the enormous number of facts which are incorporated in modern synthetic theory. The question is one of "Nothing-but," that is, whether all is said that can be said, in current theory. In opposition to the overwhelming majority of my colleagues, I don't believe so.

This is not the place for any penetrating analysis of so enormous a problem; only one particular argument incidental to questions discussed shall be made.

The transition toward higher forms of life on earth in geological history is an empirical fact. That an insect compared to a worm, man or a mammal compared to reptiles or amphibians, are "higher" forms is not a subjective value judgment, but a statement of fact that can be elaborated *ad libitum* in terms of anatomic structure, differentiation of functions, behavior, and so on. This is not contradicted by the findings that under certain conditions, such as parasitism, domestication, in cavernicolous animals and other cases retrogressive evolution is apparent; or that "living fossils" have survived unchanged, sometimes over hundreds of million of years. Under conditions of which we have a fair idea, the evolutionary process can be reversed or arrested; but this is not a disproof of the fact that, by and large, "anamorphosis" toward higher forms and functions has taken place, and is no proof that this was completely "outer-directed."

Here is the crux of the matter. Selection theory considers adaptation and evolution under the same terms of reference, both explained in terms of undirected mutation, selective advantage and differential reproduction. But adaptation to environmental conditions and evolution of forms with higher organization appear to be two different things.

I must confess that I do not see a scintilla of evidence that evolution in the sense of progression from less to more complex organisms has anything to do with improved adaptation, selective advantage, largest production of offspring, or in whatever way the Darwinian concept is couched. Adaptation to environment appears to be possible at any level of organization, as is testified by the presence, in almost any environment, of organisms belonging to many levels of organization. The problem of adaptation to a specific environment can, and has been, successfully solved by similar "technological" solutions; hence the often surprising analogies, anatomical and physiological, between organisms belonging to different classes. For this very reason, adaptation to environmental conditions cannot, to my mind, explain the historical fact that the living world did advance from lower to ever higher organizational levels. If it is said that selection directs evolution because it "increases or decreases the probability of successful reproduction" (Mayr, 1965), it is difficult to see why evolution ever progressed beyond the rabbit, the herring, or even the bacterium, which are unsurpassed in production of offspring. This doubt particularly applies to the decisive, transitional phases of evolution. The abundant remains of, say, dinosaurs testify to their well-adaptedness and profuse reproduction. The first contemporary mammals and birds (and later on protohuman forms), in contrast, apparently were highly vulnerable, adaptively undecided and weak forms, whose scanty fossil remains speak for limited numbers and not at all for a particularly high rate of reproduction.

Whether or not such considerations are accepted, they certainly pose a problem, and a fundamental one. Current theory must be reproached in that it evades discussion by way of making the problem into a spurious, and ultimately metaphysical alternative. Either, it is said, we wish scientific explanation: this is possible only by way of mutation at random and selection (plus adjunctive principles such as genetic drift, isolation, etc.). Or else we are branded as hare-brained philosophers, metaphysicists, Lamarckians and the like, believing in a Bergsonian *élan vital*, an entelechy after Driesch, a mystic drive toward perfection; that is, in anthropomorphic or finalistic agents which, in the words of Mayr (1962) "are unanimously refused by all who know anything of modern genetics." In a similar way, Simpson (1964) takes Samuel Butler as whipping boy to demonstrate the nullity of any dissident opinion; that is, a highly interesting novelist whose claims at being a biologist, however, at best rest in his having been a successful sheep farmer in Australia.

But the alternative, either "scientific" explanation by random events directed by environment, or else vitalistic (teleological, purposive, perfectionist, etc.) agents, is patently false as I have said for more than thirty years. Nobody presumes that an atom, crystal or chemical compound, is the handiwork of a vitalistic demon; but neither is it the outcome of accident. Structure and formation of physical entities at any level—atoms, molecules, high-molecular compounds, crystals, nucleic acids, etc.—follow laws which are progressively revealed by the respective branches of science. Beyond this level, we are asked to believe, there are no "laws of nature" any more, but only chance events in the way of "errors" appearing in the genetic code, and "opportunism" of evolution, "outer-directed" by environment. This is not objectively founded science, but preconceived metaphysics.

As a matter of fact, it is not difficult to point out "organismic" problems that deserve a much more careful investigation than they have received. Thus, molecular genetics has unraveled the *"vocabulary"* of the genetic code, that is, the nucleotide triplets that spell the different amino acids to be united into species-specific proteins. We do not know, at present, its *"grammar."* The genetic code, as a whole, cannot be a fortuitous sequence of "words" (nucleotide triplets)—comparable to the "word salad" produced by a schizophrenic—but must have a "meaning," spelling why species-specific proteins induced by the code and acting as enzymes are so ordered as to produce a bacterium in one case, a fly or human in others. There are good reasons to believe (which can be put forth in detail) that the code does have organizational and regulative properties, not well known at present, but indicating that not all mutations are equiprobable. Furthermore, at the organismic level, evolution is said to be "opportunistic," that is, one way is as good as the other. This is very well for structures like the horns of antelopes mentioned by Simpson, or floating devices discussed by Mayr. Human technology, however, shows that its products are not opportunistic in the sense that a given problem has any number or even a large number of equally possible solutions. A watch, an automobile, or a computer can be constructed only in certain ways; and they are certainly not constructed by tampering at random (which, of course, is the ancient argument against the chance theory of evolution). It seems that something similar applies to evolution. If an eye is to be produced, evolution has to go over the steps of light-sensitive pigment spot, cup eye and camera eye; if a respiratory pigment is needed, there are apparently only a few possible pathways leading to a small number of pigments found in the most diverse animal classes. A circulatory system, a kidney, or brain can be produced only along certain technological lines: it is not opportunistic in the sense that any construction will do. It is safe to assume that there are *evolutionary constraints* which will need more careful exploration at the various levels of organization: of viable gene mutations, of possible developmental processes, and of possible organizational configurations. This essentially emphasizes the study of *analogies* in contrast to homologies which hitherto have dominated evolutionary thinking (von Bertalanffy, 1960a). Finally, we have to look for *recurrences* and *regularities* in evolution, as was done by Rensch (1961). Principles such as that of allometric growth almost certainly belong to the laws of evolution; and there are others which, with more or less justification, can make a similar claim.

It appears, therefore, highly probable that present evolutionary theory is only a partial aspect. Instead of the empty claim that everything is explained by random mutation and selection—of what I called the Tibetan prayer wheel of selectionism (von Bertalanffy, 1960a)—there is a wealth of researchable and fascinating problems which, we believe, will open new perspectives and bring evolution into the framework of organismic and systems thinking.

Incidentally, in quite recent presentations (Mayr, 1965) we find emphasis on "organizational change in the gene complex" (*Umkonstruktion der inneren Gen-Umwelt*), consideration of the organism as an "extremely harmonious system" (*Gefüge*), on "harmony of gene function perhaps even greater than we ourselves realized 5 years ago," on "regulating genes no less important and possibly much more numerous than 'structural' genes" (which directly steer enzymatic processes), on the "unity of genotype," each hereditary characteristic being the product of successful cooperation of dozens or hundreds of genes, part of which are structural, part regulatory genes. It is worth noticing that precisely such views were advocated by me in 1949 and even 1937, in almost identical words, and long before the advent of molecular biology. I, too, emphasized "superordinate genes directing the activity of numerous other genes"; "the species as a harmoniously stabilized gene balance," "cooperation of many or all hereditary factors," "the whole organism produced by the whole genome," etc. At the time, this was completely ignored by evolutionists and sometimes ridiculed. Since then facts, of course, have immensely increased, particularly owing to the rise of molecular genetics; but the basic ideas have been vindicated. If, however, the facts indicated by Mayr are accepted, these aspects deserve emphasis and investigation equal to those given to undirected mutation and selection. Evolution then appears essentially co-determined by "internal factors" (von Bertalanffy, 1960a, p. 103; Whyte, 1965) or "inner-directed." Then the dogmatism, previously criticized, of the so-called synthetic theory becomes obsolete and the question of Evolution: Chance or Law, becomes an empirical problem needing much further investigation, but not implying unwarranted metaphysical anticipations.

This—in a very sketchy and partial outline—is about as far as science as reconstruction and interpretation of empirical data can go at present. There is another "metascientific" question, that of sense or meaning of evolution, which requires answer if we are to see in the universe something more than a game of dice (to use Einstein's well-known phrase) or a grinding machine.

In somewhat poetical form—an "unscientific interlude" as I called it—I attempted to answer the question thus:

> So evolution appears to be more than the mere product of chance governed by profit. It seems a cornucopia of *évolution créatrice*, a drama full of suspense, of dynamics and tragic complications. Life spirals laboriously upwards to higher and ever higher levels, paying for every step. It develops from the unicellular to the multicellular, and puts death into the world at the same time. It passes into levels of higher differentiation and centralization, and pays for this by the loss of regulability after disturbances. It invents a highly developed nervous system and therewith pain. It adds to the primeval parts of this nervous system a brain which allows consciousness that by means of a world of

symbols grants foresight and control of the future; at the same time it is compelled to add anxiety about the future unknown to brutes; finally, it will perhaps have to pay for this development with self-destruction. The meaning of this play is unknown, unless it is what the mystics have called God's attaining to awareness of Himself (von Bertalanffy, 1960a).

Thus, after a long detour, we have returned to our central theme of man, the problems of his existence, and his problems in this time of ours. Can we hope that in the excursion made we have gained a broader perspective, a background and scenario of the great play called the human tragicomedy?

## Spontaneous Activity

Starting our reflections, I stated somewhat boldly that certain *leitmotifs* seem to dominate recent attempts at a new and hopefully more realistic and more gratifying image of man. As everything must have a label to be talked about, I called them "symbolism" and "active personality system"—not, of course, implying that some fashionable catchwords provide any increased insight, but to indicate new frames of reference.

We have talked at some length about symbolic activities which appear to define human behavior and psychology. The other term, "active personality system," becomes more than a magic word only after the somewhat laborious inquiries we went through.

We discussed that psychology in the first half of the century was dominated by the concept of man as "robot," with the corollary of making him ever more into a robot in contemporary society. If we now propose "system" as an alternative term of reference, we know what we are talking about. We have recognized many features of "systems"—order, interaction, differentiation, regulation, self-maintenance, evolution and so forth—and this insight can be utilized for a psychology which is more adequate than previous attempts. Even more, there exists a theory of systems which, nothwithstanding its shortcomings, still is rapidly developing, is able to account for aspects previously missed, and is applied and tested in many instances. General system theory, we believe, can provide a *new framework for psychological theory*. This is a workable program whose foundations have been laid, even if its execution will require much labor in times to come (von Bertalanffy, 1966a).

There is a further term we used which appears somewhat mysterious or at least undefined, but after the previous considerations becomes understandable. We have spoken of the "active" organism, psychophysical system, or personality. Spontaneous activity is, of course, familiar to the observer of living nature. Indeed, it is the most ancient and obvious distinction between things dead and things living. The first—from a stone thrown to an elementary particle following a certain path—are set into motion only by outside forces or agents (or "passively" continue motion once started, according to the law of inertia). The latter move "under their own steam," either attracted or repelled by stimuli which figure as releasers but are not moving forces in themselves; or else in "autonomous" activities where external stimuli are absent. It is the most patent difference between a live and dead dog that the first runs around and the second doesn't; and "activity" has indeed been accepted as a token of the living state (and occasionally of life forces absent in inanimate nature) since time immemorial.

We can state quite definitely what is meant by and required for saying a system is "active." "Activity" is a consequence of the fact that the organism is an open system, able to maintain a state distant from equilibrium and to spend existing potentials. Therefore it can "act" upon releasing stimuli or in spontaneous movements. Biological, neurophysiological, ethological and psychological evidence all indicate that spontaneous activity is primary, and stimulus-response (the reflex arc in a simple case) is a regulative mechanism superimposed on it.[12]

The latter statement is, of course, a refutation of the S-R, S-O-R, or robot scheme, as the basic model of behavior. By now, the concept of "primary activity" is generally agreed upon among progressive psychologists, although terminology may be at variance and the dominating (and stultifying) influence of the S-R scheme is not overcome. I would like to mention that I emphasized "immanent activity" as part of the organismic conception in biology, long before it was recognized in psychology owing to developments such as the discovery of arousal mechanisms in the brain, active, play and exploratory behavior, Schachtel's "active and passive mode," Goldstein's and Maslow's "self-realization," the recent emphasis on "creativity," J. Bruner's educational views, and other expressions of the same trend. Here is a quotation dated 1937:

> Even under constant external conditions and in the absence of external stimuli the organism is not a passive but a basically active system. This applies in particular to the function of the nervous system and to behavior. It appears that internal activity rather than reaction to stimuli is fundamental. This can be shown with respect both to evolution in lower animals and to development . . .

and an endorsement by a leading psychologist:

> In the fundamental psychoanalytic model, there is only one basic tendency, that is toward *need gratification* or *tension reduction*. . . . Present day biologic theories emphasize the "spontaneity" of the organism's activity which is due to its built-in energy. The organism's autonomous functioning, its "drive to perform certain movements" is emphasized by Bertalanffy. . . . These concepts represent *a complete revision of the original homeostasis principle* which emphasized exclusively the tendency toward equilibrium. It is the original homeostasis principle with which psychoanalysis identified its theory of discharge of tensions as the only primary tendency (C. Bühler, 1959).

Together with the recognition of symbolism, the concept of the active as opposed to the reactive or robot organism is basic in the present reorientation of psychology. Emphasis on exploratory and play activities, the creative side of human beings, aspects that are nonutilitarian and beyond homeostasis, adaptation to external factors and the biological values of subsistence and survival—all this and more is implied in the concept of "active" organism. This, in turn, implies new practical orientation: in education, for example, emphasis on the part natural curiosity and function pleasure are playing in the learning process; new approaches in rehabilitation with emphasis on activity rather than passive repair of a damaged mental apparatus; in society at large emphasis that cultural values, far from being a luxury, belong in fact to the indispensable pillars without which human society, even in its so-called affluence and with all the gadgets provided by technology, cannot persist.

This could and should be discussed more fully. The point I wish to make is that the concept of the organism as active system puts it into the wider framework of general system theory. Let us look at some further implications deriving from our viewpoint.

## Creative Cognition

Since early times—even since ancient Leukippus and his theory of *eidola* or little pictures emitted by the things around us—psychology of cognition and epistemology were dominated by what Kaplan saucily called "the dogma of immaculate perception." The organism is a passive receiver of stimuli, sense data, information—whatever you call it—coming from outside objects; and these are—in a rather mysterious way—re-projected into space to form perceptions which more or less truly mirror the external world.

In many ways, too numerous to elaborate, modern psychology has shown that this is not so. In a very real sense, the organism *creates* the world around it. William James' "buzzing, blooming confusion" of sense data is molded, as it were, by human categories if we speak in philosophical language; in terms of psychology, by innumerable factors arising in biological evolution, in the history of culture, in the structure of language, in the individual development and learning processes of the child. The process of objectification is described in different ways in psychoanalysis (cf. Meerloo, 1956), by Werner, Piaget, Schachtel and others, which probably describe different aspects of a complex phenomenon. To quote a brief and admittedly incomplete summary (von Bertalanffy, 1964d):

> It will be correct to say that it is the general trend in modern psychology and psychiatry, supported by biological insight, to recognize the active part involved in the cognitive process. Man is not a passive receiver of stimuli coming from an external world, but in a very concrete sense *creates* his universe. This, again, can be formulated in different ways: in psychoanalytic terms as by Freud; in terms of developmental psychology according to Piaget, Werner or Schachtel; in terms of the "new look in perception" emphasizing attitudes, affective and motivational factors; by referring to von Uexküll's species-specific *umwelt*; to Cassirer's "symbolic forms"; to von Humboldt's and Whorf's evidence of linguistic (i.e., symbolic and cultural) factors in the formation of the experienced universe, etc. "The world as we experience it is the product of perception, not the cause of it" (Cantril).

The principle of the active, psychophysical organism thus pertains not only to the motoric or "output" part of behavior, but also to "input," to cognitive processes. Perception is not a passive mirroring of a world outside like a color photograph; rather, incoming informations are, by a creative act, organized into a universe. Psychology of cognition investigates the enormous number of processes concerned, physiological and psychological. For the same reason, as von Uexküll has emphasized, the experienced universes are indeed most different in an ant, frog, human baby, Australian aborigine, Athenian, medieval monk, and contemporary New Yorker.[13]

The same is true even more at the conceptual level, that is, the reconstruction of the experienced universe in symbolic systems. Here, too, it is not so that concepts, in a mysterious way, would mirror the external world. Every symbolic world, the latest and most abstract called science included, is a construct determined by innumerable factors of biological, anthropological, linguistic, and historical nature. The only limiting condition is that the construct does not too much conflict with reality "as is." For example, the mythic-magical concept of the world has served mankind quite well through hundred of thousands of years, leading even to achievements that could not be duplicated or enlarged by modern technology: The number of domesticated plants and animals has not increased since the agricultural revolution of the neolithic period. Only in the last three or four hundred years has the magical world picture been supplanted by that of science.

Such considerations from the biological standpoint surprisingly approach those in modern physics which start from quite different considerations, especially the interaction of observation and observed in microphysics (Heisenberg relation). As Heisenberg himself states, physics has given up the hope of finding "a thing in itself," such as the atom of the mechanistic universe as an ultimate reality; in quantum physics, the object of research is not nature itself any more, but man's investigation of nature. At the end of physical research, man confronts himself alone (1958; cf. von Bertalanffy, 1966b).

Among other things, the systems concept implies a new epistemology—in short, replacement of absolutistic by *perspective philosophy*.

## The Mind-Body Problem

We should not miss noting that the destruction of the dogma of immaculate perception leads to a reconsideration of that ancient riddle of philosophy, the mind-body problem (von Bertalanffy, 1964a, 1966b).

It should be apparent by now that the mind-body problem has proved to be insoluble in the ways of traditional philosophy. The centuries-old debate was little more than a mutual refutation of the classical theories of interaction, parallelism, identity, epiphenomenalism, etc.—each one demonstrated, in convincing arguments, to be untenable.

But may it not be that the mind-body problem was created by *wrong categorizations?* In one way or the other, and with whatever minor modifications, *all* theories took for granted the Cartesian dualism of matter and mind, things and consciousness, object and subject, *res extensa* and *res cogitans;* accepting them as indubitably given and trying to bring them into some intelligible relationship. By now, however, it has become obvious that neither "matter" nor "mind" stood up to the test of scientific investigation. Cartesian matter has "dematerialized" in physics—see Einstein's equation and atomic explosions. And mind, originally conceived as consciousness, has become no less problematic since the exploration of the unconscious, of which consciousness is only a minor, and possibly not the decisive fraction.

Analysis has to proceed at two levels: that of *phenomenology*, that is of direct experience, encompassing perception of outside things, feeling, thinking, willing, etc.; and of *conceptual constructs*, the reconstruction of direct experience in systems of symbols, culminating in science; it being well understood that there is no absolute gap between percept and concept, but that the two levels intergrade and interact.

Our direct experience is, of course, of things outside in space: chairs, tables, houses, stars seen in the telescope and cells in the microscope, etc., and a perceiving, feeling, thinking, willing self. But this is not a simple and ultimate "given." The experienced universe is the outcome of innumerable factors and processes by which a primitive "stream of experience" is organized and differentiated into "outside world" and "self"; processes which, as mentioned, are investigated in psychology of perception. Objectification and subjectification, the "making" of things and self, is a long and tenuous process. From a state of primary adualism (to use Piaget's term); over synesthetic and syncretic stages where percepts, concepts, emotions and motivations are interfused (about which Werner has much to say); passing animistic, mythical and magic world views, eventually the differentiation of objects and subject, material things and immaterial self arises, as experienced by the adult European. Our experienced world is the product of a long evolution, cultural history, and individual learning of the child. As psychiatrists say, the "ego boundary" is established slowly and in complex (but widely known) processes; and may again be obliterated in psychopathology.

In its phenomenological aspect, therefore, the distinction of "material things outside in space" and "immaterial feelings, thoughts, etc." is one particular mode of direct experience. Children don't have it yet; the Uexküllian *Umwelt* of animals is certainly different from ours and to be explored in each particular case; with us, essentially a visual-tactile world is concerned, and the dualism is confused in our own so-called lower senses, such as smell, taste, pain; the experience of persisting objects in an outer world is connected with concept formation and naming, as the famous awakening of Helen Keller from a dreamlike state, with formation of her first concepts, showed; and the same applies to the formation of the I or self; the world experience by the poet and mystic, of a great unity of world and self, again is somewhat different; and so on. All this amounts to saying that direct or phenomenological experience as we happen to have it, adult human beings in a certain socio-cultural situation, cannot be taken as the *sole* mode of experience, or an ultimate "given."

For this reason, it is parochial and arrogant to consider the world "as we see it"—that is, the common-sense world of the "practical" man of modern centuries—as singular point and facsimile of the "real" world; while relegating others no less intuitively convincing to other humans—such as the mythical, the Aristotelian, the artistic, the unitive knowledge of the mystic[14] —to the limbo of delusion and fancy. Rather we should recognize, in line with psychological research, linguistics, critical philosophy, modern physics, etc., that each world view is a certain *perspective* of an unknown reality, seen through the spectacles of generally human, cultural and linguistic categories.

From immediate experience man, owing to his symbolic faculties, proceeds to conceptualization. In a certain stage—roughly the post-Renaissance period—he conceptualized the two halves into which he had cut the great cake of his experienced universe, as "matter" and "mind." Well understood, there have been different conceptualizations before (and others in the offing) cutting the "cake" in other fashions:[15] for example, Plato's with immaterial ideas as true reality and perceived objects as their shadows; Aristotle's amorphous "stuff" and shaping "form," and others. These conceptualizations did not distinguish "matter" and "mind" and, based on their intuitive phenomenologic experience, couldn't do so. Only with Descartes and after, things around us were conceived as matter, ultimately atoms in space; while consciousness was hypostatized as mind, an immaterial substance to complement matter.

This worked admirably well for a long time, as testified by the success of physics and technology. Eventually, however, the conceptualization proved inadequate. Matter, originally those famous little billiard balls moving according to the laws of mechanics, has dematerialized in modern physics. We are now left with the paradox—required, however, by the progress of research—that what we perceive as solid things, chairs on which we sit and tables to put things on, "in reality" are mostly empty space, sparsely interspersed with minute centers of "energy" at astronomical distances. Speaking more properly, what is ultimately left in physics is a "something," certain structural aspects of which are describable by mathematical terms. The only "substance" (i.e., persisting entity) left is certain invariants expressed in highly abstract conservation laws, such as conservation of energy, momentum, electric charge, spin, parity, etc.

As matter dematerialized, so mind was dementalized. In a process quite similar to that of physics, reality was extended beyond the limits of direct experience. Consciousness, Descartes's *res cogitans,* is but a small sector of psychic events; unconscious happenings emerge, with quite fluid boundaries, into experienced consciousness. Again, there is a conceptual construct (called the unconscious), to account for what happens in immediate experience.

Thus present-day physics is a "science of matter" only in a Pickwickian sense. Nor is psychology a "science of the mind" as the only intuitively clear meaning of "mind"—consciousness—by no means covers the totality of "psychic" events. Matter and mind appear as conceptualizations which became inadequate with the progress of science.

Thus the construction of the world as consisting of these two components, clear enough at the time of classical physics and rationalistic psychology, has become insufficient at the levels of both phenomenology of immediate experience, and of scientific construct. Again, it appears as a "perspective," which has a definite place in history; but it would be overbearing and naïve to consider it a true representation of ultimate reality.

## Unitary Theory

If Cartesian dualism proves inadequate, what new propositions can we make regarding the relation of body and mind, physiology and psychology?

We have to remember what science—representation of the "given" in suitable conceptual constructs—actually is and means. Science, with the expansion of empirical knowledge and increasing conceptual refinement, undergoes a process of *progressive deanthropomorphization* (von Bertalanffy, 1955b). That is, with the increase of empirical knowledge and the conquest of realms far transcending everyday experience, specifically human forms of cognition and categories, adapted to dealing with the small universe of man's world of everyday, are progressively modified and eliminated. They are being replaced by constructs increasingly abstract, general, and "unvisualizable," but for this reason more apt to deal with what is beyond the world of the senses and of immediate action of the human animal. For this reason, the Aristotelian world picture—"common sense itself," as Santillana (1955) justly stated—had to go, to be replaced by the Copernican-Newtonian system which violently contradicted direct observation (after all, we *see* that the sun moves but not the earth) and was quite "unvisualizable" at the time and to Newton himself, who, as a matter of fact, never was able to understand how action at distance is possible (cf. Koyré, 1958). The same process goes on through the progress of physics, to culminate in recent times when the Kantian categories—supposedly eternal a prioris for any thinking being—had to go because all-too-human and fitting only the familiar world of medium dimensions, but not the worlds of the immensely small and immensely big which came into the field of scientific research. Hence, the things of human perception and the nice hard atoms supposedly composing them (first "visualizable" model) disappeared into clouds of abstract entities (energy, etc.) which are describable only in their formal mathematical aspects. Similarly, the space of perception and the Euclidean space of earlier physics appeared as an anthropomorphic reflection of a four-dimensional continuum, quite unvisualizable, with strange properties, but capable of encompassing a broader range of the physical world. Again, the familiar connection of cause and effect, the anthropomorphic picture of forces that push or pull, had to be replaced by the more general, abstract and deanthropomorphized scheme of statistical probability which—in the world of quanta—far exceeds "visualizability" and can only be expressed by mathematical formalism. In its deanthropomorphized form, science is a conceptual construct representing certain formal or structural relationships in an unknown X.

It appears that something similar applies to the problem we are considering. Obviously, there is an unbridgeable gap between the physical organism and the brain as a swarm of atoms or aggregate of physico-chemical processes, and the universe of direct experience, a perceived world around us, thoughts, feelings, acts of will and the like. If the brain is a "machine" (that is, an aggregate of parts following "blind" causality) the famous "ghost in the machine" is required to account for nonmechanistic features, active striving toward goals, anticipation of the future, decision processes and so forth.

This becomes different if we renounce all-too-visualizable models and concentrate on "structures," that is, abstract relationships. Then two aspects become apparent.

First, the physical (or physiological) organism appears as a highly specific organization, with such characteristics as adaptation, differentiation, goal-directed activities, dependence on future events, memory functions and the like. That is, organismic behavior appears as "ratiomorphic," occurring in a way as if it were guided by conscious "reason," although definitely it is not. Even simple actions in perception (e.g., size constancy of a perceived object although its retinal image varies) or goal-directed movements are beyond the capacities of classical machines; they appear as if they were guided by conscious intelligence—or else by an electronic computer. Lorenz (1959) has correctly emphasized that even simplest "ratiomorphic" functions require tremendous "calculating machines," far surpassing those presently constructed but realized by evolution over geological eons. The organism, far from being a collection of atoms moved by "blind" physical forces or a machine of classical physics, ever more appears as the "grand reason of the body" of which Nietzsche was speaking.

On the other hand, there is conscious experience. But this is not an isolated and well-delimited realm but rather Freud's "visible part of the iceberg." That is, conscious processes are a small portion of an unconscious manifesting itself in the little silly mistakes described in Freud's *Psychopathology of Everyday Life*, in psychophysiological regulation and up to the sublime peaks of creativity in the genius.

Psychopathology attests to the interwovenness of both halves of experience, body and mind, physiological function and consciousness. Rather brutal physical and chemical attacks—drugs, electroshock, neurosurgery—profoundly influence the "mind."

Mental events like the verbal treatment administered by the psychotherapist may profoundly influence the "body," physiological functioning including malfunction in psychoneurosis.

Thus physiological function in behavior and neurophysiology on the one hand, and psychological function in its conscious and unconscious parts on the other, begin to resemble each other ever more in their *structural aspects*. There is no sharp borderline between bodily function, unconscious and the conscious mind. In the last resort, they may be the very same thing.

Second, we have a budding, if by no means adequate or consummate, theory for aspects such as those under consideration. In certain regards, this is the theory of thinking, calculating, regulating, goal-seeking machines. Obviously, logical operation performed in consciousness and the structure and function of the brain "is" not an electronic computer with transistors, wires, currents, programs and the rest. But in their formal structure they are comparable. Similar algorithms obtain: a computer (and a brain in its "rational" aspects) is, as it were, a materialization of logical operations, and vice versa logical operations are the conceptual counterpart of the functioning of a suitably constructed computer. This correspondence is a rather deep one. Boolean algebra and binary notation used in modern computers, the functioning of synapses according to the all-or-nothing law, and Aristotelian logic in thinking are structurally the same; the same algorithm or abstract model applies.

Machines of the type discussed, however, are a genus within a more comprehensive class, called "general systems." These show characteristics such as hierarchic organization, centralization, competition and the like—again applying both to physiological and psychic events.

It is the beauty of systems theory that it is *psychophysically neutral*, that is, its concepts and models can be applied to both material and nonmaterial phenomena. This is true both of the newer kind of machines, with the logical operations, adaptation, feedback they perform; and of more general, "dynamic" systems. If both mental and behavioral or physiological events can be described by the same models, this means *isomorphism* between them. This need not be the somewhat naïve, geometrical isomorphism proposed by gestalt theory; that, for example, perception of a circle is paralleled by a geometrically similar, circular field of excitation in the brain. Coding, simulation by computers, topology, etc., have taught us much more general and sophisticated kinds of isomorphism. But, to exemplify in a special and simple case, the same flow diagram may represent on the one hand a behavioral response, and on the other the ongoing mental process. This, I repeat, is a special case for reasons that should be apparent by now. But it may exemplify the principle: that a model which is abstract and psychophysically neutral is applicable both ways.

Developments of this sort may eventually lead to a *unitary theory* (Whyte, 1960) in which "body" and "mind," in their formal or structural aspects, are comprehended by one "neutral" conceptual system. It would give no answer as to what reality really "is" (science never does) or reduce the mental to the physical (or vice versa). But we would eventually have a science in which material and mental, unconscious and conscious, physiology and psychology could be encompassed by similar, highly abstract constructs or models. Whatever else these constructs may be, the concepts of system and organization will have a central role.

## Some Views on "Culturology"

However, I still want to see how our frame of reference applies to the broadest human framework, to human groups, societies and history.

Gibbon, concluding his great work on the Roman Empire's decline and fall, wrote:

> We may acquiesce in the pleasant conclusion that every age of the world has increased and still increases the real

> wealth, its happiness, its knowledge and, perhaps, the virtue of the human race.

To us, the doctrine of what was called "perfectionism" in the eighteenth century, and "progress" in the nineteenth, appears unconvincing and frivolous. Its naïveté can hardly be better expressed than it was by Sorokin (1963):

> The whole historical process was thought of as a kind of well-ordered college curriculum, with primitive man or society as a freshman, subsequently passing through the sophomore, junior and senior classes and then graduating either in the class of "positivism" or "freedom for all"; or any other final stage suggested by the fancy and taste of the scholar.

How, then, does our systems science apply to the problem? As a matter of fact, there is an extensive body of research concerned with large systems of organisms. The study of animal populations, their growth, the competition among species and ensuing struggle for survival, of selection, isolation and other factors, is an important part of biology, with extensive experimental, wildlife and mathematical research. Systems research is also progressing in the study of human relations, which are, of course, much more complex. System principles, such as laws of growth in time or so-called allometric growth, can be applied to social constellations. For example, allometry applies as a quantitative law to business organization, to the process of urbanization, to social differentiation (cf. Naroll and von Bertalanffy, 1956; Haire, 1959). Furthermore, we have the extensive application of systems analysis to weapons systems, business, government, international politics. I, personally, am not enthusiastic about the applications of systems in industry and politics but they are a fact. The system concept is at the very center of modern sociology in doctrines such as those of Sorokin, Lévi-Strauss, Malinowski, Parsons and many others. *Sociology is the study of social systems,* whatever their exact definition may be. It may confidently be expected that general system theory will be able to provide a clear and consistent conceptual framework.

Sociology is essentially concerned with contemporary phenomena, a cross-section of human events, "synchronic" laws, as is the technical term. Can similar considerations be applied to the sequence of events in time, in longitudinal section, or to "diachronic" laws? This is the problem of a *theoretical history.*

In contrast to biological species which show evolution by way of genetic transformation, mankind presents the phenomenon of history, that is, of socio-cultural evolution. The reign of nature is dominated by laws progressively revealed in science. Are there laws of history? In view of the fact that laws are relations in a conceptual structure or theory, this question is identical with another one: Beyond description of what has happened, is theoretical history possible? If so, it should be an investigation of systems—of human groups, societies, cultures, civilizations or whatever the appropriate terms of reference may be.

A widespread conviction among historians is that this is not so. Science is said to be essentially a *nomothetic* endeavor; it establishes laws, based on the fact that events in nature are repeatable and recurrent. In contrast, history does not repeat itself. It has occurred only once; and therefore history can only be *idiographic,* that is, description of individual events that have occurred in the past. We notice that, from a formal viewpoint, the problem is identical with that of organic evolution; for, according to one opinion, evolution too is "opportunistic" and singular and therefore follows no laws.

Against this opinion—which is the orthodox one of historians—heretics have appeared who held the opposite view and, in one way or another, tried to construct theoretical history. This current started with the Italian philosopher Vico in the early eighteenth century; and was continued in the systems of Hegel, Marx, Spengler, Toynbee, Sorokin, and others. The differences among these systems are conspicuous. They all agree, however, that the historical process is not accidental but follows ascertainable laws.

Broadly speaking, it seems there are three basic aspects in history. One sees in history a *continuous progress* of mankind, often interrupted and reversed, it is true, but in its totality showing an upward course from those primitive agricultural communities in Mesopotamia in 4000 B.C. to modern jets, television and H-bombs.

The second aspect is the *cyclic* one: history is not a continuous progress of an amorphous humanity, but rather consists of a series of systems, societies or civilizations, which are distinct entities and show a lawful course of birth, development, maturity, decay and eventual decease.

Obviously the term "cyclic" should be used with discretion if at all. There are no *ricorsi* (Vico), i.e., returns to or repetitions of previous states, in any historical process, biological or human. Rather, "cyclic" should be understood as meaning fluctuations with different content, of varying duration, etc., but showing structural similarities.

The third aspect, finally, is the *existentialistic* or *nihilistic* one—in this as in other contexts, the two terms coincide. History, then, is a stream of events without law and without rhyme and reason—always the same in superficially altered guise. This was the view of Ecclesiastes in the Bible; in recent years, it found a brilliant expression in Simone de Beauvoir's *Tous les hommes sont mortels*—in my opinion, the most readable book of French existentialism, little as I like de Beauvoir's more sexy publications.

I think we can save much trouble by frankly admitting that all three aspects are apparent. There is progress in science and technology; there are cycles of primitive, mature and declining art; and perseverance of "human nature" particularly in its base aspects, war and violence.

Obviously, we can have laws only where there are recurrences. If an event happens only once, there is no law; a law only makes sense if there are similarities and repetitions that can be stated.

Theory of history, therefore, since Vico or even Plato's doctrine of the sequence of governments, always implied two considerations: first, to discover a common structure in the Protean flow of events, the many-colored, brilliant, atrocious, fascinating and depressive drama man has performed over the millennia; and second, to attribute to one's own present a definite place in the play.

The interdependence of two problems—the theoretical problem of recurrences, laws, cycles in history, and the very personal one of our own present and future—has given the dispute a bitterness otherwise lacking in scientific discussion.[16] The teachers of historical laws or cycles, Spengler and Toynbee being the best known, became prophets of doom when applying their measures to the historical present. A raw nerve was touched. The debate excited a furor, emotions and subjective judgments far exceeding dispassionate evaluation as, for somewhat different reasons, was similarly the case with Copernican and Darwinian theory. The simple expedient was to fail candidates Spengler, Toynbee *et al.* in Egyptology, Sinology, Colonial History, and any number of specialties; it was somewhat willfully forgotten that, not to speak of the almost superhuman task of universal history, professional historians are not at all agreed even about limited historical events or periods—say, Napoleonic history—where documentation is ample, happenings not remote in time, and conventional specialist methods apply. Dispassionate survey, it would appear, broadly leads to the following observations.

Glaring errors, mistakes, misinterpretations can be found in any of the "great systems"—hardly unexpected if one individual undertakes the enormous task of reviewing the whole of human history. Libraries have been written in refutation of Spengler and Toynbee. Indeed, it could be a parlor game for historians or even persons of general culture, to point out obvious errors committed by these and other historical theorists. However, looking at these shortcomings with the eye of the historian of science, we are inclined to be more lenient. Obviously, we must compare the beginnings of a "theoretical history" with pioneering attempts in other fields, rather than with conventional textbook science. In this light, Spengler is a good deal less fantastic than Kepler, less egocentric and arbitrary in his facts than Galileo. It is a *non sequitur* that, because Spengler or Toynbee erred in many respects, theoretical history is unscientific on principle and should not exist.

Beside factual, there are enormous conceptual difficulties. What are socio-cultural "systems"? How are they to be defined? Every author has made a different proposal, none unobjectionable; Kroeber and Kluckhohn (1963) enumerated some 160 definitions of "culture," and did not arive at a satisfactory one. Again, however, such difficulties are not unknown in conventional science. The concept of species in biology has been kicked around since Aristotle; and there is still no satisfactory definition. Higher taxonomic units such as genera, orders, phyla are defined differently by almost every taxonomist, as comparison of textbooks of zoology or botany may show. No great wonder, then, that Danilevsky and Spengler partitioned the much more elusive flow of history into some eight cultural entities, Toynbee into some twenty, and Sorokin used still other constructs. Paleontology is no better when the very same bones, which, in contrast to elusive cultural phenomena, anyone can see, grasp and measure, by some are attributed to dozens of species, by others lumped together in few.

In view of and fully admitting shortcomings, the great proposals of theoretical history from Vico to Sorokin come out better than one may expect in a difficult and undeveloped field. Different terms are used; different models can or even should be applied; dividing lines are drawn differently. Nevertheless, as Sorokin (1963) and Kroeber (1957) found, with all disagreements and indeed emphasizing them from their own viewpoints, there is a broad area of agreement. The consensus of writers otherwise widely separated by background, temperament, *Weltanschauung*, theory, indicates that a certain general view is correct, even if it is unpalatable to the academic establishment and to those born into a time of devaluation of values they most cherish.

Fifty years ago, Spengler demanded a true universal history, abandoning the parochial view that our own, Greco-Roman-Occidental heritage is "history" itself, encompassed in the narrow scheme of antiquity, medieval and modern periods. This has been borne out to an extent Spengler could never have expected; and, in the process, has carried away the eight or so cultures in which Spengler believed human history to be encompassed. It is a proud achievement of the past decades that, as it immeasurably increased the astronomical universe and penetrated into the subatomic world, it also gave completely new dimensions to human history. Since Schliemann's discovery of Troy and Mycenae and Evans' of the Minoic civilization, scores of lost and long-forgotten cultures have come to light. From the walls of Jericho of the eighth millennium B.C. to the skyscrapers of New York; from the strange Pietà figures of Sardinia 800 B.C. to the blood-soaked altars of pre-Columbian America; from mysterious African Zimbabwe to Scythian Siberia and its golden treasures; from the megalithic culture of the Atlantic shores with its secret Great Mother goddess to far-off Easter Island, human history and prehistory now extends over some ten thousand years, in innumerable facets, reincarnations, crests and valleys of a majestic and many-branched stream. Add to the achievements of the archaeologist's spade the work of anthropologists busily exploring what still exists of hundreds of contemporary primitive cultures; then limits, merits and the enormous difficulties of a new science of "culturology" will become apparent.

Faced with the fascinating, kaleidoscopic, brilliant—and always futile—spectacle of scores of cultures all over the globe, forgotten for millennia or still flowering before the European impact, a general thousand-years life cycle of "culture-organisms" according to Spengler, or a few "models" in Toynbee's latest proposal (1964) appear hopelessly naïve.

On the other hand, the ups and downs in history are not subjective value judgment but a fact in the public domain, remaining unaltered if, with McNeill (1963), we look at the Rise of the West rather than its Spenglerian decline. Notwithstanding the enormous expansion of the compass of historical, archaeological and anthropological research, the array of high cultures has not essentially changed, even if they may be differently defined and numbered as by Spengler, Toynbee and Sorokin.

The basic insight seems to be that history is not progress of an amorphous humanity, but is borne by a comparatively small number of socio-cultural systems, variously called cultures, civilizations, supersystems, etc. They show regularities in their development which, in a crude metaphor, are comparable to growth, maturity, decay and eventual extinction. These only have had and made history, in contrast to the hundreds of "cultures" of anthropology which remained at some paleolithic or neolithic state until Europeans brought the admirable and questionable "advances of civilization." Development and history of these "high cultures" is intimately connected with the rise of larger settlements, of "cities"; hence the English term "civilization," implying the correlation of high cultures and urbanization, is quite justified. It can hardly be doubted that in "synchronic" as well as in "diachronic" aspects socio-cultural phenomena are neither an additive result of individual actions, nor borne by an undifferentiated humanity but by super-individual "systems" whose laws are open to further investigation.

This, of course, does not say that societies or cultures are "organisms" like animals or plants, living things well separated from each other and with a predetermined life cycle. It is more the shallowness of the critics than Spengler's metaphysics which has taken a metaphor or simile for a patently absurd reality. This becomes quite clear if we remember the nature of scientific models. Every model is a conceptual representation of certain traits or formal structures of empirical entities. It leads to intellectual disaster when the model is made into metaphysical reality. This is true of any model, whether it be the billiard balls of mechanistic atomism, Descartes's animal machine, robot man of American psychology, the Freudian model of personality, culture "organisms," or whatever other model concept. If we take the theories of history as working models permitting us to see certain regularities—and, at present, very immature and contradictory models—we shall be more fair, even admitting that different models are possible and pertinent. As a matter of fact, the "organismic" model, which is a horror to historians, is well accepted in sociology, applied to such unromantic things as the growth of businesses and commercial organizations and leading to neat quantitative formulas.

Reduced to such sober terms, the mystique imbuing the work of prophets like Spengler and Toynbee, and the ire of academic history against their dilettante endeavor evaporate. There are questions amenable to scientific exploration, even though as yet treated more by outsiders of academe than by specialist professors. But then, amateurs have, in the dawn of new sciences, often played an important role before university professors and departments took over. Whether it was the early microscopists of the seventeenth century, Darwin, Mendel, Schliemann the archaeologist, or the princely collectors founding numismatics, it has happened so often that despised outsiders made the beginnings of what later became legitimate and eventually orthodox science. It appears "theoretical history," notwithstanding the protest of professionals, is in a similar position.

The definition of its theme, given by Vico 250 years ago, can hardly be improved: *una scienza nuova intorno alle comuni nature delle nazioni* and *una storia ideale eterna sopra la quale corra la storia di tutte le nazioni*. If today we speak of "models" of the historical process to be elaborated, "idealized" (as every scientific model is, starting from the most elementary ones in physics), hopefully aiming at laws, extrapolations and predictions, we use only expressions somewhat more in vogue at present. Contemporary scientists and technologists of reputation feel no inhibition nor encounter protest when forecasting the world of the year 2000 or even a million years after; not considering how much society and the world at large have changed in a few years due to inconspicuous and unpredictable events, such as the invention of the transistor and miniaturization. Predictions of the "culturologists," though harshly criticized by acadamic history, seem to have more weight and responsibility.

The most important confirmation of any theory is in its predictions. This, then, leads to the question of our own position in history. Like it or not, make any objections you please against Spengler's intuitive and "unscientific" ways, his questionable conceptualizations, his metaphysics, dogmatism and militaristic spirit; the fact remains that his predictions, made fifty years ago and long before atomic war, the emergence of the U.S.S.R. and China were even dreamt of, proved to be alarmingly correct, being verified to an extent far surpassing the success of many neat little mathematical models in vogue in modern sociology. The same even applies to Danilevsky, Spengler's obscure and little-known predecessor a hundred years ago. It seems seldom realized that titles that have become popular slogans nowadays in American sociology, from Aldous Huxley's *Brave New World* and Orwell's *1984* to Ortega's *Revolt of the Masses,* Fromm's "sick society," Riesman's "other-directed man," Whyte's *Organization Man,* Hoffer's *True Believer,* are but variations on Spenglerian themes. This is remarkable in view of the unpopularity and general ignorance of Spengler's work in the Anglo-Saxon orbit, so that direct influence or sympathy can be safely excluded; these diagnoses were, at least in part, made quite independently. The rise of mass man; authoritarianism either in the form of manifest dictators or of a pseudo-democratic power elite; the decay of creativity and arts so that, for example, it becomes impossible to distinguish allegedly serious paintings from the handiwork of a chimpanzee—this and more has become so banal that elaboration is redundant. Spengler's predictive errors (which can easily be elaborated) are few and far between in comparison.

There is no use in glossing over reality with sociological, astronautical or genetic utopias. The "Decline of the West" is not a hypothesis or prophecy; it is an accomplished fact, arrived at a somewhat earlier date than Spengler and Aldous Huxley expected. The splendid cultural development which started in the European countries aroud the year 1000 and produced Gothic cathedrals, Renaissance art, Shakespeare and Goethe, the precise architecture of Newtonian physics and all the glory of European culture—this enormous cycle of history is finished and cannot be revivified by artificial means.

So far, of course, we follow the cyclic model of history, and find in the present symptoms recurring in declining civilizations. However, in contradiction to cyclic theories of history and to the prophets of doom, we cannot miss seeing that modern civilization is *unique* in certain respects, and in this way is incomparable to the civilizations that flourished and perished in the past. The distinguishing features are quite obvious. One is *technological development*, which permits control of nature as never before achieved, making possible the replacement of an economy of want by an economy of abundance. The other is the *global nature* of our civilization. Previous ones were limited by geographical boundaries, and comprised only limited groups of human beings. Our civilization comprises the whole planet and even reaches beyond in the conquest of space. Our technological civilization is not the privilege of comparatively small societies such as the citizens of Athens or of the Roman Empire, of Germans or French, or white Europeans. Rather it is wide open to all human beings of whatever color, race or creed.

These are indeed singularities which explode the cyclic scheme of history and place our civilization at a different level from previous ones. So far as rational extrapolation is possible—that is, presupposing that no incalculable trigger event interferes, that universal atomic destruction does not take place by a failsafe accident or by the population explosion of China—the prediction seems to be rather straightforward.

We have to reckon with the stark reality of another civilization which is now emerging: a mass civilization, technological, international, encompassing the whole earth and all of mankind, in which cultural values and creativity of old are replaced by novel devices. Today's power struggles may, in their present explosive phase, lead to atomic devastation. If not, ideological and race differences will, in the long run and in one way or the other, become insignificant before the identity of material culture of industrialized mass society. The task of the individual? What is left to him is to preserve the remnants of old culture so far as mass society permits. This is not a gratifying outlook—particularly not for an unregenerate European like me—but it appears more realistic than the philosophy either of beatniks or of the prophets of paradise on earth.

## Education: Science and Humanities

Fortunately, as I said at the beginning, we are not required here to work out a theodicy or the future of man. Our objective is limited: to outline the place of psychology in modern science and briefly to review a new natural philosophy which appears to be emerging. In this sense, it is not difficult to attribute to the developments I have discussed their proper place in the history of science and philosophy.

Each historical period tries to fit together the odds and ends of its limited experience in a world view, metascience, or philosophical conception which bears close relations with the prevailing style of scientific thinking. It is again an oversimplification but nevertheless essentially correct: First came the developments of mathematics, and correspondingly philosophies after the pattern of mathematics—*more geometrico* according to Spinoza, Descartes and their contemporaries. This was followed by the rise of physics; classical physics found its world view in mechanistic philosophy, the play of material units, the world as chaos, as we have discussed. Lately, biology and the sciences of man have come to the fore. And here organization appears as the basic concept—an organismic world view taking account of those aspects of reality which were neglected previously. At the same time, this new view realizes something which previous ones, in their scientific *hubris,* had overlooked: that is, no world view, the organismic included, *is* ultimate truth or ultimate reality—every one is a perspective or an aspect, with all-too-human limitations owing to man's natural and cultural bondage. The organismic view, therefore, is at the same time *perspectivistic*—that is, aware of its limitations, not a nothing-but philosophy which believes it knows and has told everything, but tolerant of other philosophies and other experience—in arts, morals, religion—which may mirror other facets of an unfathomable reality.[17]

Although admittedly a coarse oversimplification, you will find this scheme useful. I remember the tremendous difficulties I encountered when advocating the organismic view in biology. It was wild speculation, metaphysics, empty philosophy and any bad-name traditionalists, with their fortunately limited vocabulary, were able to think of. Today it has become commonplace. Textbooks of molecular biology, biochemistry and biophysics, physiology, ecology are filled with findings about the "order and organization of parts and processes" whose investigation was the tenor of the organismic conception. The same again happened with general systems—a preposterous idea, a completely impossible enterprise (e.g., Egler, 1953)—until Research and Development offered big salaries to hire systems analysts for the philanthropic purposes of investigating improved means of destruction. It is always the story related by William James: novelties are first repudiated as nonsense; in a second stage, they are declared to be obvious and trivial; until in the third stage, the former opponents claim to have discovered them themselves.

So, when everything is said and done, and being fully aware of limitations in particular and in general, it does make some sense. What does not make sense is the world view of yesterday which has led us into a cultural wasteland and, with all gadgets provided by commercialized society, has suppressed what is human in man—a self-contradiction which necessarily has led to despair, intellectual misery, disease and delinquency. So there is meaningful work to be done. If I were talking to a German audience, I would quote Goethe—as all German professors do:

> *Noch ist es Tag, da rege sich der Mann*
> *Bald kommt die Nacht, wo niemand werken kann.**

* *Still it is day, it moves the man,*
*Soon comes the night, all silenced then.* (Author's transulation.)

This leads me to the close of my considerations. Much is spoken today about the goals of education, and especially the antagonism of science and the humanities—the Two Cultures according to C. P. Snow's rather overrated book. I would like to say that I do not see an antithesis between science and humanities. It would be easy to show, from history, that science itself is a "humanistic" endeavor, and that great leaders in science felt this way; rather than advertising profits to be expected from their research, they derived aesthetic satisfaction from it and an insight which, in abstract terms, is comparable to the mystic's unitary knowledge of reality. Speaking personally, I myself was, at different times, engaged in experiments on cell respiration or cancer, in mathematical biology, in philosophy of science, and once in a while wrote a poem—but never felt any contradiction or antithesis among such activities.

Moreover, unifying concepts, such as those of general systems theory, appear able to bridge fields traditionally subsumed under the title of science and humanities, and herald syntheses without obliterating or minimizing the profound differences that do exist in entities of the realm of science and of the socio-cultural field. In education, such concepts may contribute toward unification of knowledge, permitting us to perceive a grand plan or structure in what otherwise are different and divergent specialties (cf. Jones, in press).

The real contrast comes in only with scientism, that is, the devaluation of science to a routine job like that of the bookkeeper or mechanic, and the intrusion of scientific (or rather pseudoscientific) ways of thinking into fields of human experience where they do not belong; that positivistic, technological, behavioristic and commercialistic philosophy which devaluates man into a robot and handles him accordingly. Against this robotization of man, we may aspire toward a humanization of science. The trend we have spoken of appears to be toward science, that is, appropriate conceptual models of reality, without neglecting or denying human concerns. If this is so, science is more than an accumulation of facts and technological exploitation of knowledge in the service of the Establishment; it may still be able to present a grand view and to become deeply humanistic in its endeavor. If we achieve as much as contributing a bit toward humanization of science, we have done our share in the service of society and civilization.

# Notes

**1.** (*to p. 11*). Psychology has obviously lost the happy recklessness it enjoyed when Watson, Hull and Skinner, in their respective ways, believed they had found the great Laplacean formula of behavior, which at the same time provided the program for reorganizing society according to Hullian theory or *Walden Two* (cf. Matson, 1964). Reappraisal of what previously was accepted as dogma is going on. Even the very bulwark of "scientific" psychology—learning theory—was attacked in recent years (Miller, Gallanter and Pribram, 1960; White, 1963; Pressey, 1963) because of the recognition that instrumental conditioning (including teaching machines) falls short of "meaningful" learning in man endowed with symbolic functions.

Nevertheless, such developments appear rather as concessions hesitantly made under the impact of circumstances than as a change of heart and revision of the positivistic-behavioristic-commercialistic philosophy deeply ingrained in American life and thinking.

There is, first, the animal experiment as basis for psychological "laws" and presumably understanding human behavior, the oft-quoted brigades of rats working Skinner boxes and other contrivances. The naïve biologist is often led to wonder whether investigators using elaborate apparatus and sophisticated statistical techniques never had pets when they were children, or never looked at their animals outside the machines. Has the question been answered whether "tortured rats" or cats in the "surrealistic universe" of Thorndike boxes (Koestler, 1964) permit conclusions as to *normal* behavior? To what extent are regularities and "laws" so found not only laboratory isolates but straightforward *laboratory artifacts?* Are classical and operant conditioning, learning nonsense syllables, etc., at all applicable to normal learning processes when "structuring of perceptions," "meaning," "understanding the situation," "symbolic processes" come in; and what theory is necessary adequately to deal with them?

> The laboratory rat is confined to an artificial environment with basic needs provided for in such a manner as to render unnecessary his natural drives to exercise and the basic mechanisms for coping with environmental stress. . . . Despite the fact that the tame rat has been conditioned to an artificial diurnal cycle, this process does not alter the sensitivity of the visual receptors whose end organs are adapted to night foraging. Consequently in the normal discrimination situation carried out in photopic lighting conditions, the animal will be partially blinded by glare which is normal illumination for the experimenter. This discrimination situation is analogous, let us say for comparison, to shining bright lights into the eyes of a human subject and then requiring him to make (say) a ten-foot jump into space against closed doors. Below his starting platform, thirty feet down, is a net, and if he refuses to jump he receives a smart electric shock on the soles of his bare feet. (In addition, of course, he is continually being grasped by a giant rat over a hundred feet high.) How surprising it is that psychological experimenters have been concerned merely with what they call "right" and "wrong" responses, regardless of the internal results of intense stress (Howarth, 1954).

The outline of "robot theory" in the text is, of course, a composite picture rather than an excerpt from a specific author. It does, we believe, fairly outline the underlying philosophy of American psychology to the 1950's (roughly speaking, to the death of Hull in 1952); and since, as was said on a somewhat similar occasion (von Bertalanffy, 1960a, p. 21), "the dependence on prevailing attitudes is stronger the less it is felt," it is even now widely dominant, even though watered down and qualified. The criteria of the "robot concept" enumerated in the text can easily be found in recent literature so that it certainly cannot be said to be abandoned—with the possible exception of certain modern trends to be discussed later. The following few examples are intended more as illustration than as proof, which, in consideration of innumerable opinions and shades, is hardly possible.

*The "reactive" organism.* As Lorenz said,

> Mice must gnaw, hens must peck, squirrels hop around. They must under normal conditions in order to maintain life. But if this necessity does *not* exist under laboratory conditions, they must anyway—because all instinctive movements are produced by an internal source of stimuli, and only the now and where of their release is controlled by external stimuli (Lorenz, 1966; translation from the German, L.v.B.).

This, of course, is obvious and trivial observation; ethologists have not made a great discovery when recognizing that inner-directed activity, exploring, play and the like belong to the necessary behavioral repertoire of many species without which they would be lost and long ago extinguished in the struggle for existence; indeed no less vital than the supposedly primary drives of hunger, thirst and sex. American psychologists, conducting millions of rat experiments, were unable to see the obvious. "Until about 15 years ago these forms of behavior were overlooked in the theoretical and experimental literature" (Berlyne, 1966). "Prior to 1950, systematic investigations of these behaviors were unavailable" (Fowler, 1965, p. 3). It needed Berlyne's extensive volume (1960) and his neologism of "ludic" behavior to see the obvious; and exploratory behavior, play, etc., would probably still be "mentalistic hocuspocus" if the physiologists had not in the meantime discovered the reticular activating system, making active behavior scientifically respectable.

Similarly in educational psychology, Piaget, J. Bruner *et al.* hardly would have become fashionable if not by a rather typical "outer-directed" reaction. It may be safely assumed that the concern with "excellence," "natural curiosity," "creativity," etc., would not have arisen without the Russians' launching of Sputnik. The great educational debate and the concurrent acknowledgment of "nonphysiological" needs (e.g., striving for stimulation, information, knowledge, novelty, interest, love, manipulating drive, fun, according to Berelson and Steiner, 1964, pp. 244–249) was rather a by-product and technical question of the Cold War than a genuine reorientation.

Hardly a better example of the stultifying effect and the distortion of reality by preconceived notions could be found. Even now, "curiosity and exploratory behavior" are brought, for good or worse, into the iron scheme of drive theory (Fowler, 1965; cf. Note[12]).

*Egalitarianism and environmentalism.* It is a biological truism that living beings are different as individuals, races and species. Every owner of a dog or a budgie bird knows they are individually different; old Pavlov knew it perfectly well. Any student of elementary genetics learns that there are some five hundred mutations or races of the fruit fly, with differences not difficult to recognize. In principle, there is no problem of "nature" and "nurture" in biology, although there is a problem in each individual case. What are inherited are not phenotypic characters but potentialities (sometimes called the reaction norm) to realize characters if and when appropriate conditions are given. This ranges over the whole spectrum from "good" genes of the geneticists which phenotypically are realized under all viable conditions (e.g., blood groups) to genetic factors causing only weak dispositions, which, depending on conditions, may or may not become manifest; many hereditary diseases, possibly including schizophrenia, belong in this category.

It was up to American psychology to deny the obvious. Watson's famous dictum about the bunch of kids he could condition at will to become doctors, lawyers, beggarmen and thieves may be superannuated in view of recent study of individual differences. But even today genetic and racial differences (which are not synonymous with racism and Nazism) seem to require excuses (Hirsch, 1963).

It is a simple fact that Western peoples built Gothic cathedrals, produced the science of Galileo, Newton and Darwin and so forth; and Australian aborigines and the cannibals of New Guinea did not. (Or, as an American comedian put it, while the British still painted their bodies blue, the Jews already had diabetes.) This is not ethnocentrism, colonialism or pride in a master race (for which, in view of the mess Western society and civilization have made of the world, we would have little right indeed). But is the world, including the "developing" nations themselves, really better off when putting at the same level headhunting Borneo or warring African tribes, cow-venerating and therefore starving Indians, and the heirs of Dante, Shakespeare and Goethe, making them all "equal" and "democratic"?

According to Skinner, there is no essential difference (his expression) between cats, rats, pigeons, monkeys and man, only the latter is not so well investigated because of the disturbing prejudice of self-observation (1963, p. 336). I have a suspicion that Professor Skinner, who is by no means a mediocre mind, speaks with tongue in cheek and I would admire him for doing so. However, taking him at face value (as innumerable innocent students indubitably do), one is inclined to ask how such a statement could ever have been made.

If there are marked differences in the behavior of different fish species or between grey goose and snow goose, it would seem self-evident that somewhat greater differences exist between rats and humans. Was this trite insight of ethology heeded by experimental psychology? Apparently not; only recently, a noted primatologist found it necessary to emphasize: "Learning is part of the adaptive pattern of a species and can be understood only when it is seen as the process of acquiring skills and attitudes that are of evolutionary significance to a species when living in the environment to which it is adapted" (Washburn *et al.,* 1965). And, reviewing a recent symposium on primate behavior, Altmann (1965) stated that "most of the research reviewed [was] done by people who apparently knew little and cared less about the behavioral adaptations of their animals," thus arriving at "incredibly naïve statements" on the basis of "running rhesus and squirrel monkeys, marmosets, cats, rats and squirrels . . . completely ignoring the gross adaptive differences among these species."

*Drive theory, homeostasis and equilibrium.* In a recent symposium one of our leading psychiatrists arrived at the conclusion: "In my opinion such conditions as severe anxiety reactions, schizophrenia, paranoid states, have little to do with hunger, thirst, sex per se, but very much to do with conflict arising from the complicated conceptual world of man" (Arieti, 1965). Obviously, this statement by a noted psychiatrist was necessary in view of predominant notions, and is far-reaching in its implications. But who in his normal senses would ever have thought that one gets suicidally depressed because he is hungry or thinks he is the Emperor of China because he didn't have a girl?

The predominance of equilibrium and homeostasis notions hardly needs exemplification; they are discussed in some detail in the text.

The lack of consistent theory in psychology is often explained by emphasizing that it is a "young" science concerned with the most complex subject matter; hence its imperfections. This is a lame excuse. Heredity, for example, certainly is not a simple matter; yet Mendel's laws of 1865 are still perfectly good as far as they go. Although Mendel did not have a microscope, knew nothing about cells, nuclei or nucleic acids, his laws are basic in the fantastic development leading to molecular biology. In contrast, the "scientific" study of human behavior on an enormous scale may have 1,045 "findings established by hard evidence" (Berelson and Steiner, 1964) (with the qualification how "hard" the evidence actually is), but it has not added to the few "laws" in psychology, such as the old Weber-Fechner law and the laws of gestalt perception. The "youth" of psychology is no better excuse than the slogan of the "young country" is for corruption in Canadian and blunders in U.S. politics. As against the "new Columbianism" claimed by recent writers and justly taken to task by Sorokin (1956), psychology and sociology have quite a long history, depending on whether one lets it begin with Wundt, Fechner, Herbart, Locke or Plato. Sorokin's biting critique is confirmed by insightful psychologists:

> After making my "decision for psychology," I was impressed with the extent to which the early Greek thinkers had anticipated so much of contemporary psychology. I have never gotten over being impressed by the extent to which much contemporary research seems to be based on no recognition whatsoever of the relevance of previous thinking and research (W. A. S. Smith, 1966).

The claim that "scientific psychology" began only fifty years or so ago is a myth.

Particle physics, on the other hand, is only some twenty-five, and molecular biology hardly a dozen years old. Neither is psychology a "new" science, nor can it be claimed that behavioral scientists invented a new "scientific method." Its shortcomings are due to lack of ideas and the stultifying effect of preconceived notions, which cannot be compensated for by research on the assembly line.

It would be an equally gigantic and sterile exercise to review current psychological publications and work of departments, in order to evaluate the persistence of the "positivistic-behavioristic-commercialistic philosophy" quoted above. By and large, the judgment given in the text appears to be correct, i.e., the contention has been modified or supplemented in details without changing the basic conceptions. The reader is referred to Koestler's comments on the "Society for Prevention of Cruelty to Dead Horses" ("Appendix Two" in *The Ghost in the Machine,* presently in press) which are similar to but wittier than the above observations.

**2.** *(to p. 12).* Perhaps the reader should be reminded of some data on American "mass persuasion," for the sake of simplicity taken from Packard's *Waste Makers,* although similar facts can be collected daily from the popular press. For example, a typical American family was exposed to 1,518 selling messages in an average day; not including 16 billion pieces of advertisement per year, for which "junk mail" (third class) taxpayers had to pay $190 million to cover the deficit of the U.S. Post Office thereby arising.

Pharmaceutical firms were spending about $5,500 for every doctor in the U.S. to promote the sale of their products, employing 27,000 detail men to persuade doctors and drugstores to prescribe and sell their particular brands. In other words, (L.v.B.) while the medical profession is protesting its integrity, the doctor-patient relation, the necessity of keeping a high standard (and income deriving therefrom which, even for the most mediocre practitioner, is a multiple of that of an academic authority), the stupendous research activity of drug companies, etc., actually it is not the *doctor* who prescribes a drug according to the patient's condition and his medical knowledge, but the *salesman* (advertising artist, etc.) who has the loudest voice in the market (possibly excepting aspirin which, in American practice, appears to function as a panacea where no advertised product comes to the doctor's mind). In still other terms, the practices of Wild West quacks, bogus patent medicines, etc., have not much changed in modern practice.

"A Gallup Poll has found that most Americans questioned could not recall reading any kind of book in the past year." "Think of any important, serious book in the past year. You will not find a single copy of it *anywhere* in most of the counties of the United States, according to an estimate of the American Book Publishers Council."

"Interestingly the opprobrium generally attached to taxes [to serve old age, education, hospitals, etc.] does not apply to taxes spent to build military barracks in North Carolina or to maintain garrisons in Morocco" [rather, in 1967, to conduct the Vietnamese War] because, according to the economist, Robert Heilbroner, defense spending is an "ideal" source of economic stimulation; not only with respect to aircraft, shipbuilding, steel, construction, etc., but because, in general, public funds can be spent without trespassing into the private economy. *1984*—producing goods intended to be destroyed—is already here in 1967; war is necessary in order to keep the system going.

The system is "Free Enterprise" where, however, "twenty-five companies are issuing essentially the identical drug under twenty-five different brand names at greatly varying prices. Word artists invent the brand names, and often try to make them sound like some other highly successful drug."

Advertisers are aware of the ethical questions involved. However, in an article in *Advertising Age,* entitled *Are Advertising and Marketing Corrupting Society? It's Not Your Worry,* the Chicago marketing consultant Dr. T. Levitt concludes "that spiritual, social, moral, etc., consequences are none of [the businessman's] concern." In truth "the businessman exists for only one purpose, to create and deliver value satisfactions at a profit to himself." The parallel between consumers conditioned by advertising and Pavlov's conditioned dogs (stated in von Bertalanffy, 1956) is well known in the business. In *Printer's Ink* of January 29, 1960, the question is frankly stated: "Perhaps most important of all, [the researchers] are edging toward the ultimate question for advertising: How can the consumer, like Pavlov's dog [in 1967, owing to the advance in psychological experiment and theory, one would rather say, "like Skinner's operant conditioned rat," L.v.B.], be taught the habit of buying a specific brand?"

The conditioned stimulus is obvious; nearly all consumer behavior—cigarettes, perfumes, cars, etc.—is sex-linked (Riesman, 1964); advertising goes to the absurd length of having a beautiful maiden look at a pipette or through a new-type microscope (or else, at a roll of toilet paper or package of vaginal suppositories) with the rapture of Springlike Young Love.

In view of the above (and infinitely more that can be said to the same effect) the present writer is amply confirmed when he stated (1956) that "Return to Conditioned Reflex" of laboratory animals, and abandon of decision characteristic of man is one main feature of our time.

**3.** *(to p. 15).* This is questioned by Barnett (1967) in his critique of

Lorenz' book (1966), where he states that "nothing of the kind [i.e., social behavior of wild rats, especially "bloody mass battles"] appears in any of the detailed accounts of this species." According to Lorenz (1966, p. 158), "F. Steiniger and I. Eibl-Eibesfeldt made this important discovery [of "massacres ensuing mixing of two colonies"] at about the same time but independently of each other, Steiniger in the Brown Rat and Eibl-Eibesfeldt in the House Mouse." As both quoted are well-known ethologists (the latter known to the American public from his work on the Galapagos Islands and, incidentally, a one-time student of mine), I have no explanation for this contradiction on facts which are obviously easy to observe; except that it is symptomatic of the fight between the Anglo-Saxon behavioristic and Continental ethological schools. In this context it is interesting to note that Barnett—correctly—condemns "instinctual urges," "aggressive impulses," "threats," as "occult qualities"; failing to mention, however, that "drives," "tensions," "intervening variables," "expectation," "curiosity" and other props of "behavior theory" are of precisely the same nature.

**4.** *(to p. 24).* As an addendum to the text, I find the following statement by Portmann (1944, p. 59):

> The centers of the hypothalamic region of the diencephelon are conspicuously higher differentiated in lower animals than in anthropoids and man. Also those of monkeys are in this respect higher than the corresponding regions in the brain of anthropoids. This fact must be interpreted in connection with the impoverishment in the realm of instincts and the translation of centers for important functions into the cortex.

**5.** *(to p. 27).* A reviewer (Dettering, 1966) believes the above to be "the bravest attempt [he] knows to discuss the 'definition of symbol.'" He questions, however, whether the three criteria offered are sufficient because, according to Hayakawa, "symbols are organized into systems, which in turn means that symbols must be combined according to rules—and if they are not so combined, they become meaningless." The present author could not agree more with this but feels he has sufficiently emphasized symbol systems, their immanent laws, algorithmic character, etc. (cf. p. 29 f.). Besides, it is just conceivable that isolated symbols following the above criteria are possible; e.g., a flag language where each streamer has a meaning of its own, without relation to others and without "grammar." Possibly something comparable stood at the origin of language, e.g., some onomatopoetic utterance becoming a stand-in or symbol for an animal or happening; the "system"—grammar—arriving only later. In a broader view, however, it is readily admitted that symbols make sense or have meaning only in a wider context; a flag language makes sense only in a symbol-founded institution, called "fleet" or "marine"; and *some* implicit "system" that acoustic utterances should "stand in" for things, would seem to apply even to the remotest origins of primeval language.

**6.** *(to p. 33).* Some quotations from Werner's early work (1957) regarding his concept of "syncretism": Primitive conception has a syncretic character, i.e., motivational and affective elements are interfused with perception. Hence the objects of perception are not passive, but represent foci of dynamic powers (p. 337). Otherwise (p. 340): "Syncretism of psychic function in primitive experience—the fusion of feeling and perception, of the affective-dynamic and the perceptual-concrete, of perception and imagery." Primitive thinking is not only concrete but affective as well. It is emotionally determined insofar as it unites that which is affectively related (p. 302).

"Primitive man is certain that there is no fundamental difference between the sphere of subjective phenomena and that of (intersubjective) objective phenomena. This belief continues to hold true for the realm of magic. It is, in fact, out of this very fusion that magics and magical religious modes of thought have evolved" (p. 338f.). (The term "fusion" should better be replaced by "lack of, followed by, increasing differentiation," as was done in later publications of the Wernerian school. —L.v.B.)

"The child's concepts always have a concrete content. Image and concepts are an indivisible unity. The conceiving and the describing of a thing are not distinctly separated activities" (p. 271). The nature of speech of the child and primitive is originally "holophrastic," out of which individualized concepts and words differentiate. According to W. von Humboldt's hypothesis, "words arise by a process of gradual separation or differentiation from the (holophrastic) totality of discourse" (p. 305 f.).

**7.** *(to p. 33).* Emphasis on symbolic activities as the empirical criterion of human as contrasted with animal behavior does not, of course, depreciate the unconscious and what is permanent in Freud's work. "Creative" processes (Koestler's "bisociation") generally take place at an unconscious level and in the way of averbal and syncretic concepts which only slowly crystallize. This is presumably the meaning of the obscure concept of "intuition," which is rather unanimously recognized by creative scientists as source of their conceptual discoveries (cf. Sorokin's temperamental defense, 1962, as an example for many similar statements) leading to breakthroughs, while it is abhorred by empiricists—both in science and history—who consider it thoroughly "unscientific" and, bound by a positivist metaphysics, appear to know little about what actually happened in the history of science and scientific discovery. Conscious symbolic activity, particularly application of an algorithm already given in language, mathematics, arts, music, etc., in this sense (not quite corresponding to Freudian usage) is "secondary process." It is indeed a main and well-known criticism against Freud that to him, the unconscious is an "attic" where repressed sexual trash is stored; in contrast to previous explorers of the unconscious (Novalis, Eduard von Hartmann, Bergson and others) who emphasized the unconscious as a *creative force* (cf. Whyte, 1960); a bad misunderstanding (or "repression") of obvious fact only slowly remedied in recent developments. Some of the bases of the development of symbolic activities in unconscious processes are discussed in the text.

**8.** *(to p. 36).* L. Mumford, in a book presently in press (1967) has arrived at essentially the same conclusions:

> On this reading, the evolution of language—a culmination of man's more elementary forms of expressing and transmitting meaning—was incomparably more important to further human development than the chipping of a mountain of hand-axes. Besides the relatively simple coordinations required for tool-using, the delicate interplay of the many organs needed for the creation of articulate speech was a far more striking advance. This effort must have occupied a greater part of early man's time, energy, and mental activity, since the ultimate collective product, spoken language, was infinitely more complex and sophisticated at the dawn of civilization than the Egyptian or Mesopotamian kit of tools (p. 7).
>
> The remarkable fact about [the rise of civilization] technically is that it was the result, not of mechanical inventions, but of a radically new type of social organization: a product of myth, magic, religion, and the nascent science of astronomy. This implosion of sacred political powers and technological facilities cannot be accounted for by any inventory of the tools, the simple machines, and the technical process then available. Neither the wheeled wagon, the plow, the potter's wheel, nor the military chariot could of themselves have accomplished the mighty transformations that took place in the great valleys of Egypt, Mesopotamia, and India, and eventually passed, in ripples and waves, to other parts of the planet.
>
> The study of the Pyramid Age I made in preparation for writing "The City in History" unexpectedly revealed that a close parallel existed between the first authoritarian civilizations in the Near East and our own, though most of our contemporaries still regard modern technics, not only as the highest point in man's intellectual development, but as an entirely new phenomenon. On the contrary, I found that what economists lately termed the Machine Age or the Power Age, had its origin, not in the so-called Industrial Revolution of the eighteenth century, but at the very outset in the

organization of an archetypal machine composed of human parts (p. 9).

**9.** *(to p. 58).* It is gratifying to an author and scientist when ideas advanced by him become anonymous, which indicates that they have become part of current thought. It is irritating when such ideas are introduced as if they were new, and their origin is conveniently "forgotten." Therefore, a few data on the development of the "organismic conception in biology" which (as mentioned in the text) are generally acknowledged and oft-quoted in international literature (additional quotations in von Bertalanffy, 1960a).

Whitehead's *Science and the Modern World* was published in 1925. The present author's first studies were published in 1926, and the organismic conception summarized in *Kritische Theorie der Formbildung* of 1928 (English: *Modern Theories of Development,* 1933; available in paperback, 1962).

Cannon's concept of homeostasis was formulated in 1929 and 1932. Approximately contemporaneous was Ritter and Bailey's historically important study on the "organismal" conception (1928), and the work of Woodger, Wheeler and others. The homeostasis concept and organismic thought reach back, of course, to Claude Bernard's *fixité du milieu intérieur*. Bernard's work was, however, little known in the German-speaking countries at this time; the present writer was not influenced by it. He further developed the organismic idea in *Theoretische Biologie* of 1932 (2nd vol., 1942, 1951). The idea of "general system theory" was conceived by the author in the 1930's, and first pronounced in lectures 1937 and later. Owing to laboratory work and other circumstances, the first printed communications were after the war (1945 ff.). Contemporary were Ashby's first studies (e.g., 1945), independently arriving at similar conclusions; Lotka's work (1925) was the first precursor. Wiener's *Cybernetics* appeared in 1948, making the term (previously used by Ampère early in the eighteenth century) popular and starting the cybernetic movement in engineering, social science and biology; although (widely unknown in America) feedback models of physiological phenomena had been advanced much earlier by R. Wagner in the middle '20's, and by Hess (e.g., 1942). General system theory found its organ in the Society for General Systems Research founded by von Bertalanffy, Boulding, Gerard and Rapoport in 1954 (affiliated to the AAAS).

**10.** *(to p. 66).* The best surveys of biocybernetics are by Hassenstein (1960, 1966); *Progress in Biocybernetics* (ed. by Wiener and Schadé; since 1964) publishes special investigations as are also found in many other places.

**11.** *(to p. 73). General Systems* (ed. by von Bertalanffy and Rapoport;

since 1956) is the best introduction to general system theory and its various applications.

**12.** *(to p. 89).* Since the facts basic for the "primacy of activity" in the organism and behavior vs. reactivity are not generally known among psychologists, a brief résumé appears to be in place.

In evolution, it appears that spontaneous activity preceded reaction to stimuli (and, of course, learned behavior and conditioning). The normal state of a paramecium, for example, is not one of rest but of continuous movement (Jennings). Rather than the reflex arc, like the knee jerk as simplest example (or the nerve-muscle preparation), rhythmic-automatic movements, e.g., of a medusa (or else the vertebrate heart) appear to be the most primitive prototype of animal behavior.

Neurophysiology comes to a similar conclusion. Primitive locomotive activities are caused by central automatisms that do not need external stimuli and therefore are preserved in the disafferentiated animal; the reflex is not the primary element of behavior but a device for adapting primary automatisms to changing peripheral conditions (von Holst, 1937).

Similarly, in embryonic development, the first movements of an embryo or fetus (axolotl, cat, human, etc.) are spontaneous "mass movements" and appear before reflex arcs are established. For a comprehensive survey of older results, cf. Herrick, 1956; the discussion of S-R theory from the biological viewpoint in von Bertalanffy 1960a (taken over from 1937) is still essentially correct.

The more recent discovery of the reticular (and other) activating systems of the brain stem is well known (Magoun, 1958). It again emphasized the activity of the nervous system in contrast to reactivity and S-R scheme.

Instinctive or innate behavior, according to Lorenz, is based upon innate releasing mechanisms (IRM); that is, instinctive behavior is normally triggered by stimuli, but in their absence may 'go off" spontaneously in so-called in-vacuo or driving-idle reactions, as when a bird not provided with nest-building materials performs the behavior, i.e., the innate sequence of nest-building movements, anyway, into "clear air" with nothing to build with.

Biologically, therefore, the S-R model, i.e., the conception of the living organism as a system in "equilibrium," and reaction to stimuli as the prototype of behavior is unfounded.

In mammals and man, the importance of "spontaneous" activities (i.e., activities not caused by external stimuli, not conditioned or learned, often nonutilitarian and not rewarded by food, drink, sex, etc.), e.g., play and exploratory behavior, "curiosity," is increasingly recognized.

"Play" activity at the highest level (cf. Huizinga, 1955), that is, at the symbolic level characteristic of man, is human "culture," which may have utilitarian applications (technology) but in its roots ("basic" against applied science, art, religion, mystic experience) is not conditioned by external constraints or gratification of biological needs, and sometimes is directly contrary to biological satisfaction, survival of the individual or group, and other "biological values" (cf. p. 39 ff.). One may say that Toynbee's challenge-and-response metaphor is more characteristic of human behavior than the S-R scheme: mountain peaks (space, the atom, the viler aspects of human nature, and what not) "are there" to be conquered, they are not unconditioned or conditioned stimuli causing behavior in order to restore disturbed psychological or social "equilibrium."

For reasons previously mentioned, it was an unexpected shock to American psychology when the obvious was discovered, e.g., that the S-R, need-gratification "machine" of a hungry rat may prefer exploration of its environs to food, that it explores without being conditioned by a reward, etc. Because upsetting the S-R applecart, the detailed studies by Berlyne, the Harlows and others were needed to show what would be obvious from observation of a rat's natural behavior. Fowler (1965, p. 23) neatly expresses the embarrassment of conventional psychology: "The task of defining curiosity and exploration seems difficult if not impossible, for there appears to be no goal object or condition to and for which the organism responds." Voices seeing in a rat's "curiosity and exploratory behavior" not a mystery (which was created only by the prejudicial *a priori* that the rat *should* be an S-R machine), but something perfectly natural and even trivial, were few and far between. For example, Arnold's (1960, p. 223) statement much resembling that quoted in the text (von Bertalanffy, 1960a and 1937):

> Whenever motivation is explained as the result of instincts, drives, needs, stimuli, or homeostatic mechanisms, the organism is assumed to be a *passive reactive system*, energized by these motives. (Recently several theorists have pointed out that motives are not "energizers," notably Maslow (1954), McClelland *et al.* (1953), and Hebb (1949). They have argued that the organism is already active and that motives merely direct its activity.) The analogy of the organism with an inanimate object or a system of forces obviously stems from the conception, dating back to classical physics, that an object is at rest unless a force is applied to move it. Today, since subatomic physics has accustomed us to the ceaseless activity of electrons, neutrons, and protons within the atom, an activity not set in motion by external forces, it should be much easier to concede that living things have intrinsic activity. In fact, the very definition of a living being is *that of a self-maintaining, self-repairing, self-moving system.*

This she based on the then recent discovery of the reticular activating system. Similar is G. Allport's heretical but rather obvious finding (1961, p. 90) that

> the healthy child and adult are continually building up tensions, in the form of new interests, and are going way beyond the basic, safely established level of homeostasis; acquiring knowledge for its own sake, creation of works of beauty and usefulness, love, sense of duty, etc., cannot be reduced to drive psychology.

Although Arnold (1960, p. 223) had already stated that "starting with the assumption of inherent activity rather than reactivity, we do not have to look for special driving forces, be they instincts, drives, or needs that spur the living being to action," Fowler (1965) in his recent text (destined for undergraduates) still makes a desperate attempt to bring, with the help of innumerable, complicated and contradictory rat experiments, "curiosity and exploratory behavior" into the safe fold of drive theory—not noticing that the very notions of curiosity, exploration, novelty, boredom, meaningfulness, etc., belong to the "mentalistic nonsense" which should have no place in objective "behavior theory"; and that "drives" are mythological beings whose explanatory value is precisely zero when they are adjusted *a posteriori* and epicycle-like, to what experiments (frequently contradicting each other) may present.

**13.** *(to p. 92).* The neo-Wernerian approach to cognition (attempting to integrate the study of perceptual operations with sensory-motor and conceptual-symbolic operations) was summarized by Wapner (1965) in a series of "don't" statements and their organismic-developmental counterparts:

(1) The organism should not be considered as a passive recipient of stimuli; rather, cognition implies organismic activity ("equilibration" between stimulus-input and the state of the organism). (2) The relationship between means and ends is not one-to-one; rather, (a) a cognitive "goal" can be achieved by different means; and (b) one "means" can serve to different ends. (a) especially refers to developmental stages: sensory-motor, perceptual and conceptual-symbolic operations; (b) to "overextension" of functions, e.g. overextension of tactual definition of objects so that the latter can be replaced by the visual mode. (3) Intentions of the organism toward the world are not invariant; rather, self-world intentions vary, and so does cognition influenced by these intentions or attitudes. (4) The theory of perceptual development should not be restricted to perception because the latter is closely linked to sensory-motor behavior on the one hand, and conceptual-symbolic on the other. (5) It should not be restricted to one sensory modality, especially vision, as this is a late and unique development in evolution; lower, tactual-kinesthetic senses must equally

be taken into account. (6) Such theory should not be restricted to ontogenetic change; the term, "development" means an idealized change (increase in differentiation and hierarchic integration or "orthogenetic principle") equally applicable to general psychology, psychopathology, action of psychopharmacological drugs, regression, aging, etc. (7) Similarly, such theory is not restricted to progressive or regressive changes in time, but also should be applicable to organismic stratification of cognitive operations at a given state.

Wapner's study has to be consulted for experimental support of these theses, especially with respect to the "polarization" of self and object. It should be apparent, however, how close the similarity is between the "organismic-developmental approach" in psychology, based upon psychological observation and experiment; and the contentions of the present author who, being a practicing biologist, formulated his ideas without the benefit of psychological experimentation and intimate knowledge of recent developments in the latter science.

The above also implies a revision of the concept of "projection," both in the sense of traditional theory of perception and epistemology (the images on the retina are "projected" into space), and of "understanding the other mind" (empathy), including Freudian projection (we "project" our feelings, etc. into the other human being, but also into animals and—in animistic thought—into anything else in the world). *In contrast*, perception of objects is not projection of retinal images, empathy not projection of our emotions; rather, self and things, I and Thou crystallize or differentiate from a primitive syncretic, synesthetic and adualistic experience. For this reason, empathy is not a complex "inference" of "other minds" from behavioral manifestations but something very primitive or primeval, more highly developed in primitives and presumably animals than in civilized man. The fact that animism and panpsychism anthropologically precede complex processes of inference and a "soulless" world, and a similar sequence in child psychology, is a confirmation of the latter view, and refutation of the theory of projection. Therefore critique of the "dogma of immaculate perception" implies not only revision of conventional psychology of cognition and epistemology, but also of Freudian theory, which in this respect is anchored in conventional thought.

**14.** *(to p. 95).* As a concise statement of the mystic's view: "Ultimate reality is incommensurable with our own illusoriness and imperfection; for intellectual operations depend upon language, and our vocabulary and syntax were evolved for the purpose of dealing precisely with that imperfectness and illusoriness, with which God is incommensurable. Ultimate reality cannot be understood except intuitively, through an act of will and the affections" (A. Huxley, 1945).

**15.** *(to p. 96).* The culture-boundness and language-boundness of human universes (perceived and conceptual) is a special case of the various experienced universes, *Umwelten* (von Uexküll) or ambients of animals which are determined by their receptor-effector structures. Each *Umwelt* is a particular reflection, sector or aspect of "reality"; not a mirroring of "reality" itself, but isomorphic to it to such extent as to make survival possible. (Cf. von Bertalanffy, 1955b.)

**16.** *(to p. 105).* It may be interesting to note that the furor created by Spengler's work (1918) in Germany after its defeat in the First World War was exactly repeated by Toynbee's tremendous popular success when the Second War did not establish the American Century and the World of Rooseveltian Freedoms. Also, only in the latter period of disappointment did Spengler's work achieve a modest success in the U.S. (Bagby, 1958; Hughes, 1958, 1962; Sorokin, 1963; Mazlish, 1966). For a number of reasons, the present writer's predilection is for the first of the pair. Among them is early preoccupation with Spengler's work (cf. von Bertalanffy, 1924); the fact that Spengler is the original and Toynbee a rather pale copy; that, compared to Spengler's spectacular vision of epochs past, Toynbee is flat and pedestrian; that Spengler is concerned with "culture" in all its glittering facets while Toynbee's *History* (as he himself admits) only consists of political struggles and religion. Their faults, on the other hand, are identical; therefore the "Fight about Spengler" (Schröter, 1922 and 1949) around 1920 was repeated, with often literally identical arguments, in the enormous dispute about Toynbee in the forties and fifties. Spengler's frank admission that "intuition" is his method is preferable to Toynbee's protestations of his allegedly "empirical" method; by the nature of things, a "model" (in whatever scientific endeavor) comes forward first in the way of a vision or "intuition," and never results from a mere collection of "facts" as Toynbee, following the line of English empiricism, pretends. Spengler's Twilight-of-the-Gods eschatology is, as recent history proves, somewhat nearer to reality than Toynbee's chiliasm under the banner of a diluted high-church Christianity.

Spengler's *Untergang* (*Decline* is a pallid translation) was experienced, in Germany around 1920, as a shock and sudden attack on the most cherished values and ideals of humanity in progress; until, with the disappointments and humiliations to follow, people got used to live with and love bombs, beatniks, underdeveloped nations, war against poverty in supposedly Affluent Society and other Discontents of Civilization. It was rather recently discovered that the Spenglerian prophecy was not the spleen of a mad German *Gymnasium* professor but that he was a link in a long chain of partly highly reputable thinkers. The germinal idea goes back as far as Vico. Danilevsky's pre-emption of most Spenglerian ideas in 1869 was rediscovered only recently. Jacob Burckhardt, Nietzsche ("nihilism"), Dilthey, Henry Adams, and others, not to mention Marx, were well conscious of the "decline of the West" as was Dostoevsky on the other side of the fence. Oscar Wilde's and Beardsley's *fin du siècle—fin du monde* was the artistic expression of the same phenomenon. So was, in terms of science, the breakdown of the Newtonian universe, the marvelous world constructed after the principles of rationalism and deism of the High Baroque; countersigned, as it were, by Freud, Pareto, Sorel, etc., with the additional clause how little "rational" man, society and history are. Spengler and Toynbee should not have been received as newfangled "prophets of doom," products of Prussian militarism and its defeat, or of later crises and neo-Christian missionarism; they were, with all their shortcomings, embedded in a long tradition.

**17.** *(to p. 113).* Leibniz', Nietzsche's, Dilthey's, Sorel's and Ortega y Gasset's views are related to "perspective" philosophy. The author's contentions, however, developed from his biological studies, without (at least consciously) being influenced by the above.

# Bibliography

In keeping with the intentions of the present study and the ideas discussed which often cannot be allocated to one special source, the following bibliography contains, beyond publications explicitly cited in the text, a limited number of works important for the development of a "humanistic psychology." It is unnecessary to emphasize that no attempt whatever toward complete listing was made; nor does citation (or lack of it) imply a value judgment. The reader interested in some topic may, however, find the bibliography useful as a guide for further study.

Ackoff, R. L. "Games, Decisions, and Organizations." *General Systems,* 4, 145–150, 1959.

——. "Systems, Organizations, and Interdisciplinary Research." *General Systems*, 5, 1–8, 1960.

Afanasjew, W. G. "Über Bertalanffys 'organismische' Konzeption." *Deutsche Zeitschrift für Philosophie,* 10, 1033–1046, 1962.

Allport, G. W. *Becoming*. New Haven: Yale University Press, 1955.

——. *Pattern and Growth in Personality*. New York: Holt, Rinehart and Winston, 1961.

Altmann, S. A. "Primate Behavior in Review." *Science*, 150, 1440–1442, 1965.

Anderle, O. F. "Theoretische Geschichte. Betrachtungen zur Grundlagenkrise der Geschichtswissenschaft." *Historische Zeitschrift*, Heft 185/1, 1–54, February, 1958.

Anonymous. "Crime and the Great Society." *Time*, March 24, 1967, 22–23.

Arieti, S. "Contributions to Cognition from Psychoanalytic Theory." In G. Masserman (ed.), *Science and Psychoanalysis*, Vol. 8. New York: Grune and Stratton, 1965.

Arnold, M. B. *Emotion and Personality*. Vol. 1: *Psychological Aspects*. New York: Columbia University Press, 1960.

Ashby, W. R. "Effect of Controls on Stability." *Nature*, 155, 242–243, 1945.

——. "Constraint Analysis of Many-Dimensional Relations." *Technical Report*, 2, Air Force Office of Scientific Research, 1964.

Bagby, P. *Culture and History*. London: Longmans, Green, 1958.

Barnard, C. I. *Elementary Conditions of Business Morals*. Committee on the Barbara Weinstock Lectures. Berkeley: University of California, 1958.

Barnett, S. A. "On the Hazards of Analogies Between Human Aggression and Aggression in Other Animals." *Scientific American*, 216, No. 2, 135–148, Feb. 1967.

Beadle, G. W. *Genetics and Modern Biology*. Philadelphia: American Philosophical Society, 1963.

Beauvoir, S. de *Tous les hommes sont mortels*. Paris: Gallimard, 1946.

Bendmann, A. "Die 'organismische Auffassung' Bertalanffys." *Deutsche Zeitschrift für Philosophie*, 11, 216–222, 1963.

Berelson, B., and G. A. Steiner. *Human Behavior: An Inventory of Scientific Findings*. New York/Burlingame: Harcourt, Brace & World, 1964.

Berlyne, D. E. *Conflict, Arousal, and Curiosity*. New York: McGraw-Hill, 1960.

——. "Curiosity and Exploration." *Science*, 153, 25–33, 1966.

Bertalanffy, L. von. "Einführung in Spenglers Werk." *Literaturblatt Kölnische Zeitung,* May, 1924.

——. *Nikolaus von Kues.* München: G. Müller, 1928.

——. *Theoretische Biologie.* Bd. I, II. Berlin: Borntraeger, 1932, 1942; 2nd ed. Bern: Franke, 1951.

——. *Das Gefüge des Lebens.* Leipzig: Teubner, 1937.

——. "Der Organismus als physikalisches System betrachtet." *Die Naturwissenschaften,* 28, 521–531, 1940.

——. "Zu einer allgemeinen Systemlehre." *Blätter für deutsche Philosophie,* 18, 3/4, 1945. Extract in *Biologia Generalis,* 19, 114–129, 1949.

——. "The Theory of Open Systems in Physics and Biology." *Science,* 111, 23–29, 1950a.

——. "An Outline of General System Theory." *British Journal for Philosophy of Science,* 1, 139–164, 1950b.

——. "Theoretical Models in Biology and Psychology." In D. Krech and G. S. Klein (eds.), *Theoretical Models and Personality Theory.* Durham: Duke University Press, 1952.

——. *Biophysik des Fliessgleichgewichts.* Translated by W. H. Westphal. Braunschweig: Vieweg, 1953. Revised ed. with W. Beier and R. Laue. In preparation.

——. "General System Theory." *Main Currents in Modern Thought,* 11, 75–83, 1955a. Reprinted in *General Systems,* 1, 1–17, 1956. R. W. Taylor (ed.), *Life, Language, Law: Essays in Honor of A. F. Bentley.* Yellow Springs, Ohio: Antioch Press, 1957, pp. 58–78.

——. "An Essay on the Relativity of Categories." *Philosophy of Science,* 22, 243–263, 1955b. Reprinted in *General Systems,* 7, 71–84, 1962.

——. "A Biologist Looks at Human Nature." *Scientific Monthly,* 82, 33–41, 1956. Reprinted in R. S. Daniel (ed.), *Contemporary Readings in Psychology.* 2nd ed. Boston: Houghton Mifflin, 1965, pp. 267–275. S. J. Beck and H. B. Molish (eds.), *Reflexes to Intelligence, A Reader in Clinical Psychology.* Glencoe, Ill.: Free Press, 1959.

——. "Comments on Aggression." *Bulletin of the Menninger Clinic,* 22, 50–57, 1958.

——. "Human Values in a Changing World." In A. H. Maslow

(ed.), *New Knowledge in Human Values*. New York: Harper & Brothers, 1959, pp. 65–74.

——. *Problems of Life*. (1949). New York: Harper Torchbooks, 1960a.

——. "Principles and Theory of Growth." In W. W. Nowinski (ed.), *Fundamental Aspects of Normal and Malignant Growth*. Amsterdam: Elsevier, 1960b.

——. "The Psychopathology of Scientism." In H. Schoeck and J. W. Wiggins (eds.), *Scientism and Values*. Princeton, N.J.: Nostrand, 1960c, pp. 202–218.

——. *Modern Theories of Development* (1928). Translated by J. H. Woodger (1933). New York: Harper Torchbooks, 1962a.

——. "General System Theory—A Critical Review." *General Systems*, 7, 1–20, 1962b.

——. "The Mind-Body Problem: A New View." *Psychosomatic Medicine*, 24, 29–45, 1964a.

——. "Basic Concepts in Quantitative Biology of Metabolism." *Helgoländer wissenschaftliche Meeresuntersuchungen*, 9, 5–38, 1964b.

——. "The World of Science and the World of Value." *Teachers College Record*, 65, 496–507, 1964c.

——. *Cognitive Processes and Psychopathology*. Address at Symposium of Academy of Psychoanalysis, Montreal, December 26, 1964d.

——. "On the Definition of the Symbol." In J. R. Royce (ed.), *Psychology and the Symbol: An Interdisciplinary Symposium*. New York: Random House, 1965a, pp. 28–71.

——. "Zur Geschichte theoretischer Modelle in der Biologie." *Studium Generale*, 5, 290–298, 1965b.

——. "Professor Bernhard Rensch zum 65. Geburtstag." *Naturwissenschaftliche Rundschau*, February, 1965c.

——. "General System Theory and Psychiatry." In S. Arieti (ed.), *American Handbook of Psychiatry*, Vol. 3. New York: Basic Books, 1966a, pp. 705–721.

——. "Mind and Body Re-Examined." *Journal of Humanistic Psychology*, 6, 113–138, 1966b.

——, and A. Rapoport. *General Systems*. Yearbooks of the Society for General Systems Research. Ann Arbor, Mich.: Braun-Brumfield, 11 vols., 1956ff.

Blandino, G., S.J. *Problemi e Dottrine di Biologia Teorica*. Bologna: Minerva Medica, 1960.

Boguslaw, W. *The New Utopians*. Englewood Cliffs, N.J.: Prentice-Hall, 1965.

Boulding, K. E. *The Image*. Ann Arbor: University of Michigan Press, 1956.

Bronowski, J. "Review of 'Brains, Machines and Mathematics' by M.A. Arbib." *Scientific American,* 130–134, July, 1964.

Bugental, J. F. T. "Humanistic Psychology and the Clinician." *Progress in Clinical Psychology*, 223–239, 1966.

Bühler, C. "Theoretical Observations About Life's Basic Tendencies." *American Journal of Psychotherapy*, 13, 561–581, 1959.

——. *Psychologie im Leben unserer Zeit.* München-Zürich: Knaur, 1962.

Bühler, K. *Die Krise der Psychologie*. Jena: Fischer, 1927.

——. *Sprachtheorie*. Jena: Fischer, 1934.

——. "Von den Sinnfunktionen der Sprachgebilde." In R. Wisser (ed.), *Sinn und Sein.* Ein Philosophisches Symposium. Tübingen: Max Niemeyer, 1960, pp. 95–112.

Cannon, W. B. "Organization for Physiological Homeostasis." *Physiological Reviews*, 9, 1929.

——. *The Wisdom of the Body*. New York: Norton, 1932.

Carter, L. J. "Systems Approach: Political Interest Rises." *Science*, 153, 1222–1224, 1966.

Cassirer, E. *The Philosophy of Symbolic Forms.* 3 vols. New Haven: Yale University Press, 1953, 1955, 1957.

——. *The Individual and the Cosmos in Renaissance Philosophy* (1927). Translated by M. Domandi. New York: Harper Torchbooks, 1963.

Chomsky, N. " 'Verbal Behavior' by B. F. Skinner." *Language,* 35, 26–58, 1959.

Commoner, B. "In Defense of Biology." *Science*, 133, 1745–1748, 1961.

De-Shalit, A. "Remarks on Nuclear Structure." *Science*, 153, 1063–1067, 1966.

Dettering, R. "More Symbolic Synthesis." *Etc.: A Review of General Semantics,* 23, 268–275, 1966.

Dobzhansky, T. "Are Naturalists Old-Fashioned?" *American Naturalist,* 100, 541–550, 1966.

Dubos, R. "Environmental Biology." *BioScience,* 14, 11–14, 1964.

——. " 'We Are Slaves to Fashion in Research!' " *Scientific Research,* 36–37, 54, January, 1967.

Egler, F. E. "Bertalanffian Organismicism." *Ecology,* 34, 443–446, 1953.

Ertel, S. "Der Symbolcharakter künstlicher Lautgebilde." *Psychologische Forschung,* 28, 491–518, 1965.

Fowler, H. *Curiosity and Exploratory Behavior.* Toronto: MacMillan, 1965.

Frank, L. K. "Man's Changing Image of Himself." *Zygon.* Journal of Religion and Science, 1, 158–180, 1966.

Frankl, V. E. "Das homöostatische Prinzip und die dynamische Psychologie." *Zeitschrift für Psychotherapie und Medizinische Psychologie,* 9, 41–47, 1959.

——. "Irrwege seelenärztlichen Denkens. Monadologismus, Potentialismus und Kaleidoskopismus." *Der Nervenarzt,* 31, 385–392, 1960.

Glass, B. "The Ethical Basis of Science." *Science,* 150, 1254–1261, 1965.

Goldstein, K. *The Organism.* New York: American Book Company, 1939.

Gray, W., N. D. Rizzo and F. D. Duhl (eds.) *General Systems Theory and Psychiatry.* New York: Little, Brown. In press.

Gross, L. (ed.) *Symposium on Sociological Theory.* Evanston, Ill.: Row, Paterson, 1959.

Guilford, J. P. "Intelligence: 1965 Model." *American Psychologist,* 21, 20–26, 1966.

Haase, R. "Der Zweite Hauptsatz der Thermodynamik und die Strukturbildung in der Natur." *Die Naturwissenschaften,* 44, 409–415, 1957.

Hacker, F. "Psychology and Psychopathology of Symbolism." In J. R. Royce (ed.), *Psychology and the Symbol.* New York: Random House, 1965, pp. 73–87.

Haire, M. "Biological Models and Empirical Histories of the Growth of Organizations." In M. Haire (ed.), *Modern Organization Theory*. New York: Wiley, 1959, pp. 272–306.

Hall, A. D. *A Methodology for Systems Engineering*. Princeton, N.J.: Van Nostrand, 1962.

——, and R. E. Fagen. "Definition of System." *General Systems*, 1, 18–28, 1956.

Hanika, F. de P. *New Thinking in Management*. London: Hutchinson, 1965.

Harris, E. E. *The Foundations of Metaphysics in Science*. London: Allen and Unwin, 1965.

Hart, H. "Social Theory and Social Change." In L. Gross (ed.), *Symposium on Sociological Theory*. Evanston, Ill.: Row, Paterson, 1959, pp. 196–238.

Hassenstein, B. "Die bisherige Rolle der Kybernetik in der biologischen Forschung." *Naturwissenschaftliche Rundschau*, 13, 349–355; 373–382; 419–424, 1960.

——. "Kybernetik und biologische Forschung." In L. von Bertalanffy and F. Gessner (eds.), *Handbuch der Biologie*. Bd. I, Heft 26–30. Frankfurt a.M.: Athenaion, 1966, pp. 629–730.

Hebb, D. O. "Drives and the C.N.S. [Conceptual Nervous System]." *The Psychological Review*, 62, 243–254, 1955.

Heisenberg, W. *Physics and Philosophy: The Revolution in Modern Science*. New York: Harper and Brothers, 1958.

Hempel, C. G. *Aspects of Scientific Explanation and Other Essays in the Philosophy of Science*. New York: Free Press, 1965.

Henry, J. *Culture against Man*. New York: Random House, 1963.

——. "Review of 'Human Behavior: An Inventory of Scientific Findings,' by Berelson and Steiner." *Scientific American*, 129–134, July, 1964.

Herrick, C. J. *The Evolution of Human Nature*. New York: Harper Torchbooks, 1956.

Hess, W. R. "Biomotorik als Organisationsproblem." (Parts I and II.) *Die Naturwissenschaften*, 30, 441–448, 537–541, 1942.

Hirsch, J. "Behavior Genetics and Individuality Understood." *Science*, 142, 1436–1442, 1963.

Holst, E. von. "Vom Wesen der Ordnung im Zentralnervensystem." *Die Naturwissenschaften,* 25, 625–631; 641–647, 1937.

Howarth, E. "A Note on the Limitations of Externalism." *Australian Journal of Psychology,* 6, 76–84, 1954.

Hughes, H. S. *Consciousness and Society.* New York: Knopf, 1958.

——. *Oswald Spengler* (1952). New York: Scribner Library, 1962.

Huizinga, J. *Homo Ludens.* Boston: Beacon Press, 1955.

Huxley, A. *Grey Eminence* (1941). New York: Meridian Books, 1959.

——. *Perennial Philosophy.* New York: Harper and Brothers, 1945.

Jakobson, R. "Why 'mama' and 'papa'?" In B. Kaplan and S. Wapner (eds.), *Perspectives in Psychological Theory. Essays in Honor of Heinz Werner.* New York: International University Press, 1960.

Jones, R. G. "Holism, the Integration of Knowledge, and Liberal Education." *Second Synopsis Congress of the International Society for the Comparative Study of Civilizations,* Salzburg, Austria, September, 1964. In press.

——. "Meta-Culture, Types of Society, and Education." *Interdisciplinary Conference on the Modern Conception of Primary General Education.* Prague, March, 1966. In press.

Kainz, F. *Die Sprache der Tiere.* Stuttgart: Enke, 1961.

Kamarýt, J. "Ludwig von Bertalanffy a syntetické směry v závapadné biologii." In J. Kamarýt (ed.), *Filosifické problémy moderní biologie.* Prag: Ceskoslovenské Akademie, 1963, pp. 60–105.

Kanaev, I. I. *Aspects of the History of the Problem of the Morphological Type from Darwin to the Present.* In Russian. Moscow-Leningrad: *NAUKA,* 1966, pp. 193–200.

Kaplan, B. "An Approach to the Problem of Symbolic Representation: Nonverbal and Verbal." *Journal of Communications,* 11, 52–62, 1961.

——. "The Comparative-Developmental Approach and its Application to Symbolization and Language in Psychopathology." In S. Arieti (ed.), *American Handbook of Psychiatry,* Vol. 3. New York: Basic Books, 1966, pp. 660–688.

Kaufmann, W. *Existentialism from Dostoevsky to Sartre.* New York: Meridian Books, 1957.

Kepes, G. (ed.), *Sign, Image, Symbol.* New York: Braziller, 1966.

Koestler, A. *The Act of Creation.* New York: Macmillan, 1964.

——. *The Ghost in the Machine.* London: Hutchinson. In press.

Koyré, A. *From the Closed World to the Infinite Universe.* New York: Harper Torchbooks, 1958.

Kroeber, A. L. *Style and Civilizations.* Ithaca, N.Y.: Cornell University Press, 1957.

——, and Cl. Kluckhohn. *Culture. A Critical Review of Concepts and Definitions* (1952). New York: Vintage, 1963.

Kubie, L. "The Distortion of the Symbolic Process in Neurosis and Psychosis." *Journal of the American Psychoanalytic Association,* 1, 59–86, 1953.

Langer, S. K. *Philosophy in a New Key* (1942). New York: Mentor Books, 1948.

Lenneberg, E. H. "A Note on Cassirer's Philosophy of Language." *Philosophy and Phenomenological Research,* 15, 512–522, 1955.

Lorenz, K. "Methods of Approach to the Problems of Behavior." *The Harvey Lectures,* 1958–1959. New York: Academic Press, 1960, pp. 60–103.

——. "Gestaltwahrnehmung als Quelle wissenschaftlicher Erkenntnis." *Zeitschrift für experimentelle und angewandte Psychologie,* 6, 118–165, 1959.

——. *On Aggression.* New York: Harcourt, Brace & World, 1966.

Lotka, A. J. *Elements of Mathematical Biology* (1925). New York: Dover, 1956.

McNeill, W. *The Rise of the West.* Chicago: University of Chicago Press, 1963.

Magoun, H. W. *The Waking Brain.* Springfield, Ill.: Charles C. Thomas, 1958.

Maloney, J. C. "Advertising Research and an Emerging Science of Mass Persuasion." *Journalism Quarterly,* 41, 517–528, Autumn, 1964.

Maritain, J. *Three Reformers. Luther—Descartes—Rousseau.* New York: Scribner's, 1950.

Maslow, A. H. "Cognition of Being in the Peak Experiences." *Journal of Genetic Psychology*, 94, 43, 1959.
——. *Toward a Psychology of Being*. New York: Van Nostrand, 1962.
Matson, F. W. *The Broken Image*. New York: Braziller, 1964.
Mazlish, B. *The Riddle of History*. New York: Harper & Row, 1966.
Mayr, E. "Zufall oder Plan, das Paradox der Evolution." In *Evolution und Hominisation*. Stuttgart: G. Fischer, 1962, pp. 21–35.
——. "Selektion und die gerichtete Evolution." *Die Naturwissenschaften*, 52, 173–180, 1965.
McLuhan, M. *Understanding Media: The Extension of Man*. New York: McGraw-Hill, 1964.
Menninger, K., with M. Mayman, and P. Pruyser. *The Vital Balance*. New York: Viking Press, 1963.
Meerloo, J. A. M. "Pavlovian Strategy as a Weapon of Menticide." *The American Journal of Psychiatry*, 110, 809–813, 1954.
——. *The Rape of the Mind*. Cleveland: World Publishing Company, 1956.
Mesarovič, M. D. "Foundations for a General Systems Theory." In M. D. Mesarovič (ed.), *Views on General Systems Theory*. New York: Wiley, 1964, pp. 1–24.
Miller, G. A., E. Galanter, and K. H. Pribram. *Plans and the Structure of Behavior*. New York: Holt, 1960.
Miller, G. A. "A. Koestler's View of the Creative Process." *Scientific American*, 211, 145–149, May, 1964.
Muller, H. J. *The Uses of the Past* (1952). New York: Mentor Books, 1960.
Mumford, L. *The Myth of the Machine*. Technics and Human Development. New York: Harcourt, Brace & World, 1967.
Murray, H. "The Personality and Career of Satan," *Journal of Social Issues*, 18, 36–54, 1962.
Naroll, R. S. and L. von Bertalanffy. "The Principle of Allometry in Biology and the Social Sciences." *General Systems*, 1, 76–89, 1956.
Nash, H. "Critique and Comment. The Role of Metaphor in

Psychological Theory." *Behavioral Science*, 3, 336–345, 1963.

Peller, L. E. "Language and its Prestages." *The Bulletin of the Philadelphia Association for Psychoanalysis*, 14, 55–76, 1964.

Piaget, J. *The Construction of Reality in the Child.* New York: Basic Books, 1959.

Portmann, A. *Biologische Fragmente zu einer Lehre vom Menschen.* Basel: Schwabe, 1944.

Pressey, S. L. "Teaching Machine (and Learning Theory) Crisis." In E. J. Shoben and F. L. Ruch (eds.), *Perspectives in Psychology.* Chicago: Scott, Foresman and Company, 1963, pp. 126–130.

Rapoport, A. "Uses and Limitations of Mathematical Models in Social Sciences." In L. Gross (ed.), *Symposium on Sociological Theory.* Evanston, Ill.: Row, Paterson, 1959, pp. 348–372.

——. "Mathematical Aspects of General Systems Theory." *General Systems*, 11, 3–11, 1966.

Rensch, B. "Die Abhängigkeit der Struktur und der Leistungen tierischer Gehirne von ihrer Grösse." *Die Naturwissenschaften*, 45, 145–154, 1958.

——. "Die Evolutionsgesetze der Organismen in naturphilosophischer Sicht." *Philosophia Naturalis*, 6, 289–326, 1961.

Repge, R. "Grenzen einer informationstheoretischen Interpretation des Organismus." *Giessener Hochschulblätter*, 6, 1962.

Riesman, D. "Two Generations." *Daedalus.* Journal of the American Academy of Arts and Sciences, 93, 711–735, 1964.

Ritter, W. E. and E. W. Bailey. *The Organismal Conception.* University of California Publications in Zoology, 31, 1928.

Rothschuh, K. E. *Theorie des Organismus.* 2nd ed. München, Berlin: Urban & Schwarzenberg, 1963.

Royce, J. R. "Psychology at the Crossroads between the Sciences and the Humanities." In J. R. Royce (ed.), *Psychology and the Symbol: An Interdisciplinary Symposium.* New York: Random House, 1965, pp. 3–25.

Santillana, G. de. *The Crime of Galileo.* Chicago: University of Chicago Press, 1955.

Schachtel, E. G. *Metamorphosis.* New York: Basic Books, 1959.

Schröter, M. *Metaphysik des Untergangs* (1922). München: Leibniz, 1949.

Simpson, G. *This View of Life*. New York: Harcourt, Brace & World, 1964.

Skinner, B. F. *Verbal Behavior*. New York: Appleton-Century-Crofts, 1957.

——. "The Flight from the Laboratory." In M. Marx (ed.), *Theories in Contemporary Psychology*. New York: Macmillan, 1963, pp. 323–338.

Smith, W. A. S. "Philosophical Psychology and the History of Psychology." *Newsletter*. Division 24 of the American Psychological Association, 1, no. 4, 1966.

Sorokin, P. A. *Fads and Foibles in Modern Sociology*. Chicago: Regnery, 1956.

——. "Mutual Convergence of the United States and the U.S.S.R. to the Mixed Sociocultural Type." *Mémoire du XIXe Congrès de Sociologie*, México, D. F., 3–46, 1961. Reprinted in *The Basic Trends of Our Times*. New Haven, Conn.: College and University Press, 1964, pp. 78–130.

——. "The Factor of Creativity in Human History." *Main Currents in Modern Thought*, 18, 99–104, 1962.

——. *Modern Historical and Social Philosophies* (1950). New York: Dover, 1963.

——. *Contemporary Sociological Theories* (1928). New York: Harper Torchbooks, 1964.

——. "Sociology of Yesterday, Today and Tomorrow." *American Sociological Review*, 30, 833–843, 1965.

——. *Sociological Theories of Today*. New York, London: Harper & Row, 1966.

Spengler, O. *Der Untergang des Abendlandes*. 2 vols. (1918, 1922), 82nd and 116–118th ed. München: Beck.

Stachowiak, H. "Gedanken zu einer allgemeinen Theorie der Modelle." *Studium Generale*, 18, 432–463, 1965.

Tillich, P. "Is a Science of Human Values Possible?" In A. H. Maslow (ed.), *New Knowledge in Human Values*. New York: Harper & Brothers, 1959, pp. 189–196.

Toynbee, A. *A Study of History*. Vol. 12, Reconsiderations. New York: Oxford University Press, 1964.

Tribiño, S. E. M. G. de. *Una Nueva Orientación de la Filosofía Biológica: El Organicismo de Luis Bertalanffy*. Primer premio

"Miguel Cané." Buenos Aires: Cursos y Conferencias, 28, 1946.
Trincher, K. S. *Biology and Information.* New York: Consultants Bureau, 1965.
Ungerer, E. *Die Wissenschaft vom Leben.* Eine Geschichte der Biologie. Bd. III. Freiburg/München: Alber, 1966.
Vico, G. *The New Science* (1744). Translated by T. G. Bergin and M. H. Fish. New York: Doubleday, 1961.
Wagner, F. *Die Wissenschaft und die gefährdete Welt.* München: C. H. Beck, 1964.
Wapner, S. "Some Aspects of a Research Program Based on an Organismic-Developmental Approach to Cognition: Experiments and Theory." *Journal of the American Academy of Child Psychiatry*, 3, 193–230, 1964.
——. "An Organismic-Developmental Approach to the Study of Perceptual and Other Cognitive Operations." In C. Scherer (ed.), *Cognition: Theory, Research, Promises.* New York: Harper & Row, 1964.
——. "An Organismic-Developmental Approach to Perceived Body: Object Relations." In Noël Jenkin, and R. H. Pollack (eds.), *Perceptual Development: Its Relation to Theories of Intelligence and Cognition.* Proceedings of a Conference Sponsored by the Institute for Juvenile Research, Illinois State Department of Mental Health and National Institute of Child Health and Human Development, National Institutes of Health, 1965.
Washburn, S. L., P. C. Jay, and J. B. Lancaster. "Field Studies of Old World Monkeys and Apes." *Science,* 150, 1541–1547, 1965.
Weaver, W. "Science and Complexity." *American Scientist*, 36, 536–644, 1948.
Weisskopf, W. A. "Comment." In A. H. Maslow (ed.), *New Knowledge in Human Values.* New York: Harper & Brothers, 1959, pp. 199–223.
Werner, H. *Comparative Psychology of Mental Development* (1940). Revised ed. New York: International Universities Press, 1957.

—— and B. Kaplan. *Symbol Formation.* New York: Wiley, 1963.

White, R. W. "Motivation Reconsidered: The Concept of Competence." In E. J. Shoben and F. L. Ruch (eds.), *Perspectives in Psychology*. Chicago: Scott, Foresman and Company, 1963, pp. 33–59.

Whyte, L. L. *The Unconscious Before Freud.* New York: Basic Books, Inc., 1960.

——. *Internal Factors in Evolution.* New York: Braziller, 1965.

Wiener, N. *Cybernetics.* New York: Wiley, 1948.

—— and J. P. Schadé. *Progress in Biocybernetics.* Amsterdam, London, New York: Elsevier Publishing Company, 1964 ff.

Wolstenholme, G. (ed.), *Man and his Future.* London: Ciba, 1963.

# Index